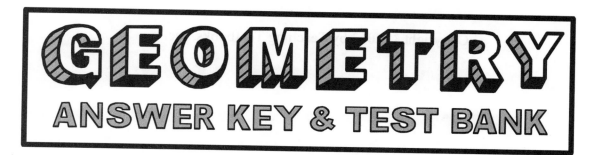

Table of Contents

Geometry: A Teaching Textbook™
2.0 Version
Answer Key and Test Bank
Greg Sabouri and Shawn Sabouri

Printed in the United States of America.

ISBN: 978-0-9835812-7-7

Teaching Textbooks, Inc.
P. O. Box 16310
Oklahoma City, OK 73113
www.teachingtextbooks.com

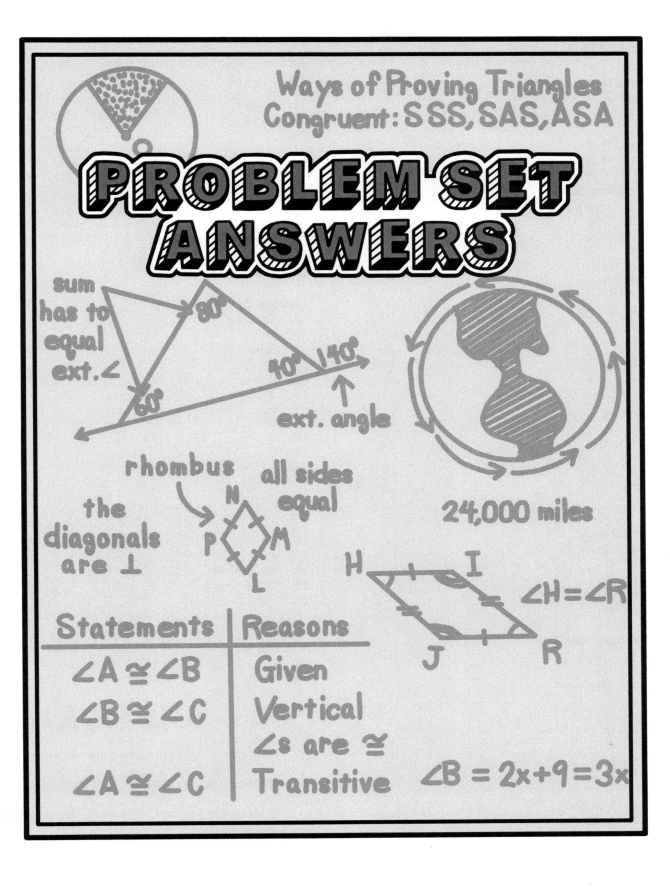

Ways of Proving Triangles
Congruent: SSS, SAS, ASA

PROBLEM SET ANSWERS

sum has to equal ext. ∠

80°

40° 140°

60°

ext. angle

rhombus

the diagonals are ⊥

all sides equal

N
P   M
L

24,000 miles

H   I
      J   R
∠H = ∠R

Statements	Reasons
∠A ≅ ∠B	Given
∠B ≅ ∠C	Vertical ∠s are ≅
∠A ≅ ∠C	Transitive

∠B = 2x+9 = 3x

CHAPTER 1

Practice 1
a. A
b. D
c. C
d. B
e. D

Problem Set 1
1. True
2. True
3. False
4. False
5. B
6. A
7. C
8. C
9. A
10. D
11. B
12. A
13. A
14. C
15. A
16. D
17. A
18. C
19. A
20. B

Practice 2
a. Deductive
b. C
c. A
d. Invalid
e. D

Problem Set 2
1. True
2. True
3. False
4. E
5. D
6. B
7. B
8. C
9. B
10. A
11. Inductive
12. Deductive
13. Inductive

14. A
15. C
16. E
17. A
18. Invalid
19. Valid
20. D
21. D

Practice 3
a. D
b. B
c. Invalid
d. A
e. Self-evident

Problem Set 3
1. True
2. True
3. False
4. A
5. B
6. B
7. C
8. E
9. E
10. C
11. A
12. B
13. Invalid
14. Valid
15. D
16. D
17. A
18. Self-evident
19. Self-evident
20. Not self-evident

Practice 4
a. D
b. Invalid
c. Valid
d. E
e. If Melanie wins her match, then she'll be in the semi-finals.
    If Melanie is in the semi-finals, then she'll have to play on Saturday.
    If Melanie plays on Saturday, then she'll be too tired.
    If Melanie is too tired, then she'll lose in the semi-finals.

Problem Set 4

1. True
2. True
3. True
4. C
5. D
6. A
7. D
8. E
9. B
10. B
11. C
12. A
13. A
14. Invalid
15. Valid
16. D
17. E
18. A
19. D
20. If the team wins the game, they'll be in the playoffs.
    If the team is in the playoffs, they'll have to play in Dallas.
    If the team plays in Dallas, the fans will be against them.
    If the fans are against the team, the team will lose in the playoffs.
21. If the flowers aren't watered, they will wither.
    If the flowers wither, they'll have to be thrown away.
    If the flowers are thrown away, they can't be shown at the wedding.
    If the flowers aren't shown at the wedding, the bride will be upset.

Practice 5

a. D
b. C
c. Invalid
d. B
e. If Mrs. Johnson has the driveway redone, Mr. Johnson will get wet cement on his shoes.
   If Mr. Johnson gets wet cement on his shoes, he will also get some on Mrs. Johnson's new carpet.
   If Mr. Johnson gets wet cement on Mrs. Johnson's new carpet, she will hit him over the head with a frying pan.
   If Mrs. Johnson hits Mr. Johnson over the head with a frying pan, he will have to go to the emergency room.

Problem Set 5

1. True
2. True
3. False
4. A
5. B
6. C
7. B
8. B
9. A
10. E
11. E
12. C
13. D
14. E
15. Invalid
16. Invalid
17. C
18. D
19. D
20. A
21. If Twila Glisten points to the grand prize, then the audience will say "ooh" and "ahh."
    If the audience says "ooh" and "ahh," then contestant #3 will get nervous.
    If contestant #3 gets nervous, then he will miss the question.
    If contestant #3 misses the question, then he will be the runner-up.
22. If the florist delivers the roses to the wrong office, Jane will think she has a secret admirer.
    If Jane thinks she has a secret admirer, she will make a hair appointment for tomorrow.
    If Jane makes a hair appointment for tomorrow, she will have to postpone her Christmas shopping again.
    If Jane postpones her Christmas shopping again, she will end up wrapping presents on Christmas Eve.

CHAPTER 2

Practice 6
a. C
b. E
c. C
d. A
e. Invalid

Problem Set 6
1. False
2. True
3. A
4. E
5. C
6. C
7. D
8. B
9. B
10. C
11. B
12. A
13. D
14. E
15. D
16. C
17. B
18. Valid
19. Invalid
20. Invalid
21. E
22. A
23. D
24. If the rebels enter the demilitarized zone tomorrow, then negotiations will break down.
If negotiations break down, then the government will attack.
If the government attacks, then the rebels will be crushed.
If the rebels are crushed, then all hope for democracy is lost.

Practice 7
a. No
b. No
c. point S
d. Valid
e. D

Problem Set 7
1. True
2. True

3. True
4. A
5. B
6. No
7. No
8. Yes
9. No
10. point D
11. point C
12. point F
13. E
14. B
15. E
16. E
17. A
18. C
19. Invalid
20. Valid
21. B
22. D
23. D
24. A

Practice 8
a. B
b. Yes
c. No
d. A
e. E

Problem Set 8
1. True
2. True
3. C
4. E
5. B
6. D
7. D
8. C
9. Yes
10. No
11. A
12. A
13. A
14. B
15. C
16. D
17. Invalid
18. Valid
19. A
20. E

21. If the auctioneer raises the bid for the painting, then Mrs. Higgins will drop out.
    If Mrs. Higgins drops out, then Rutherford will win the auction.
    If Rutherford wins the auction, the proceeds will go to the library.
    If the proceeds go to the library, then the library will be able to build a new wing.
22. D
23. B

Practice 9
a. C
b. B
c. No
d. Invalid
e. A

Problem Set 9
1. True
2. True
3. B
4. A
5. D
6. D
7. 1
8. 0
9. 2
10. E
11. C
12. E
13. D
14. A
15. B
16. E
17. Yes
18. No
19. Invalid
20. Valid
21. C
22. D
23. D
24. C

Practice 10
a. B
b. D
c. A
d. E
e. Invalid

Problem Set 10
1. False
2. True
3. True
4. C
5. C
6. A
7. E
8. D
9. E
10. B
11. D
12. B
13. E
14. B
15. A
16. C
17. Valid
18. Invalid
19. D
20. C
21. If the batter hits a double, then he'll drive in one run.
    If the batter drives in one run, then the Tigers will win the playoffs.
    If the Tigers win the playoffs, then the city will celebrate.
    If the city celebrates, then the street cleaners will have to work overtime.
22. E
23. A

Practice 11
a. $m\angle BOC = 70$
b. A
c. C
d. C
e. C

Problem Set 11
1. True
2. False
3. A
4. B
5. A
6. C
7. A
8. E
9. E
10. $m\angle LOM = 120$
11. $m\angle POM = 25$
12. $m\angle LOP = 95$
13. A

14. C
15. C
16. Yes
17. A
18. C
19. B
20. Invalid
21. Invalid
22. If the cat burglar leaves his flashlight, then the maid will think something is wrong.
If the maid thinks something is wrong, then she will check the safe.
If the maid checks the safe, then she will find it open.
If the maid finds the safe open, then she will faint.
23. E
24. B

Practice 12

a. A

b. $m\overline{PQ} = 2\frac{1}{7}$

c. $QR = 5$

d. $m\angle QPD = 36$

e. $m\angle BCV = 28$ and $m\angle VCE = 28$

Problem Set 12

1. True
2. False
3. True
4. C
5. A
6. E
7. C
8. D
9. D
10. E
11. B
12. A
13. $m\overline{ST} = 5\frac{1}{4}$
14. $FG = 8$
15. $JK = 3$
16. $m\angle RYZ = 48$
17. $m\angle ABD = 16$
18. $m\angle MOL = 37$ and $m\angle LOP = 37$
19. A
20. A
21. A
22. C

23. A
24. C
25. C

Practice 13

a. A

b. $UI = 6\frac{1}{4}$

c. $CN = 5.85$

d. $m\angle PQR = 28$

e. Invalid

Problem Set 13

1. True
2. True
3. A
4. A
5. D
6. D
7. D
8. C
9. E
10. E
11. A
12. C
13. $FJ = 4\frac{1}{4}$
14. $m\overline{DE} = 7.5$
15. $AP = 7.45$
16. $m\angle AOY = 23$
17. $m\angle EFG = 36$
18. B
19. A
20. Invalid
21. Valid
22. E
23. E

CHAPTER 3

Practice 14
a. B
b. A
c. $HJ = 2.5$
d. $MO = 28.2$
e. (2) $\overline{WO}$ bisects $\angle TOS$.

   (3) $m\angle 1 = \frac{1}{2} m\angle UOR$

   (4) Definition of an angle bisector
   (5) Given

   (6) $\frac{1}{2} m\angle UOR = \frac{1}{2} m\angle TOS$

   (7) Substitution Property

Problem Set 14
1. True
2. True
3. A
4. C
5. C
6. D
7. A
8. E
9. B
10. D
11. B
12. A
13. $m\angle WNY = 59$
14. $BC = 8.9$
15. $QB = 2.7$
16. $UW = 24.6$
17. $m\angle ABW = 38$
18. $m\angle LMN = 58$
19. D
20. B
21. Valid
22. Valid
23. C
24. E
25. (2) $\overline{AB}$ bisects $\angle DBC$.
    (3) Definition of an angle bisector

    (4) $m\angle 2 = \frac{1}{2} m\angle DBC$

    (5) Given
    (6) Multiplication Property
    (7) $m\angle 1 = m\angle 2$

Practice 15
a. A

b. C
c. $x = 2$
d. complement: 30
e. (1) Given
   (2) Betweenness of Rays
   (3) Given
   (4) Definition of a right angle
   (5) Substitution Property
   (6) Definition of complementary angles

Problem Set 15
1. False
2. True
3. B
4. D
5. D
6. B
7. E
8. C
9. A
10. E
11. E
12. B
13. A
14. $m\angle BPC = 38$
15. $x = 3$
16. complement: 60
17. complement: 40
18. complement: 40
19. A
20. B
21. Invalid
22. Invalid
23. (1) Given
    (2) Betweenness of Rays
    (3) $\angle ZOX$ is a right angle.
    (4) Definition of a right angle
    (5) Substitution Property
    (6) $\angle ZOY$ and $\angle YOX$ are complementary.

Practice 16
a. E
b. B
c. $x = 20$
d. A
e.

Statements	Reasons
1. $\overline{GD}$ bisects $\angle EDF$.	1. Given
2. $m\angle 3 = m\angle 4$	2. Definition of an angle bisector
3. $\angle 1$ and $\angle 3$ are supplementary.	3. Given

Statements	Reasons
4. ∠2 and ∠4 are supplementary.	4. Given
5. $m\angle 1 = m\angle 2$	5. Supplements of equal angles are equal.

Problem Set 16

1. True
2. False
3. D
4. D
5. E
6. complement: 65
   supplement: 155
7. complement: 2
   supplement: 92
8. C
9. B
10. D
11. B
12. B
13. $x = 34$
14. $y = 37$
15. A
16. A
17. $y = 3$
18. B
19. E
20. C
21. A
22. C
23.

Statements	Reasons
1. $\overline{MO}$ bisects $\angle NPQ$.	1. Given
2. $m\angle NPO = m\angle OPQ$	2. Definition of an angle bisector
3. $\angle NPO$ and $\angle NPM$ are supplementary.	3. Given
4. $\angle OPQ$ and $\angle QPM$ are supplementary.	4. Given
5. $m\angle QPM = m\angle NPM$	5. Supplements of equal angles are equal.

Practice 17

a. C
b. E
c. $m\angle AXB = 40$
d. $EG = 2$

e.

Statements	Reasons
1. ∠5 and ∠6 are a linear pair.	1. Given
2. ∠5 and ∠6 are supplementary.	2. If two angles are a linear pair, then they are supplementary.
3. ∠4 and ∠6 are supplementary.	3. Given
4. $m\angle 4 = m\angle 5$	4. If two angles are supplementary to the same angle, then they are equal.

Problem Set 17

1. True
2. False
3. B
4. D
5. B
6. E
7. A
8. A
9. D
10. A
11. D
12. $z = 21$
13. $x = 61$
14. B
15. $m\angle DOE = 30$
16. C
17. $AB = 4$
18. $x = 115$
19. $y = 65$
20. $z = 115$
21. Invalid
22. Valid
23.

Statements	Reasons
1. ∠2 and ∠3 are a linear pair.	1. Given
2. ∠2 and ∠3 are supplementary.	2. If two angles are a linear pair, then they are supplementary.
3. ∠1 and ∠3 are supplementary.	3. Given
4. $m\angle 1 = m\angle 2$	4. If two angles are supplementary to the same angle, then they are equal.

Practice 18

a. A
b. $m\angle KOJ = 53$

c. 60
d. B
e. Statements

Statements	Reasons
1. $\angle ABO$ is complementary to $\angle AOB$.	1. Given
2. $\angle CDO$ is complementary to $\angle DOC$.	2. Given
3. $m\angle AOB = m\angle DOC$	3. Pairs of vertical angles are equal.
4. $m\angle ABO = m\angle CDO$	4. If two angles are complementary to equal angles, then they are equal.

Problem Set 18
1. True
2. True
3. E
4. E
5. C
6. D
7. complement: 43
   supplement: 133
8. B
9. C
10. B
11. E
12. $m\angle AOD = 49$
13. $m\angle AOB = 131$
14. $m\angle DOC = 131$
15. 33
16. 72
17. $m\angle BOC = 65$
18. $RT = 40$
19. $m\angle EOG = 58$
20. $KM = 20$
21. B
22. B
23. Statements

Statements	Reasons
1. $\angle 1$ is complementary to $\angle 3$.	1. Given
2. $\angle 2$ is complementary to $\angle 4$.	2. Given
3. $m\angle 1 = m\angle 2$	3. Pairs of vertical angles are equal.
4. $m\angle 3 = m\angle 4$	4. If two angles are complementary to equal angles, then they are equal.

Practice 19
a. E
b. $m\angle KOJ = 108$
c. 34
d. $m\angle NPL = 54$
e. Valid

Problem Set 19
1. True
2. False
3. C
4. D
5. B
6. A
7. E
8. A
9. D
10. D
11. C
12. $m\angle EPF = 112$
13. $m\angle DPE = 68$
14. 56
15. 69
16. $PB = 21$
17. $m\angle SQT = 63$
18. A
19. D
20. Valid
21. Valid
22. Statements

Statements	Reasons
1. $m\angle 1 = m\angle 4$	1. Given
2. $m\angle 1 = m\angle 2$	2. Pairs of vertical angles are equal.
3. $m\angle 3 = m\angle 4$	3. Pairs of vertical angles are equal.
4. $m\angle 4 = m\angle 2$	4. Transitive Property
5. $m\angle 2 = m\angle 3$	5. Substitution Property

Practice 20
a. B
b. $m\angle HKL = 72$
c. 121
d. A
e. Invalid

Problem Set 20
1. False
2. False
3. D
4. A

5. D
6. B
7. E
8. A
9. C
10. C
11. C
12. complement: 69
    supplement: 159
13. D
14. $m\angle ABC = 84$
15. $m\angle BEF = 64$
16. 75
17. 137
18. E
19. D
20. Invalid
21. Invalid
22. **(2)** Given
    (4) $m\angle ACB = 90$
    (5) $m\angle ACB = m\angle 1 + m\angle 2$
    (6) Substitution Property

Practice 21

a. D
b. $m\angle MOL = 60$
c. 105
d. A
e.

Statements	Reasons
1. $\overline{LM} \perp \overline{MN}$, $\overline{PN} \perp \overline{MN}$, $\angle 5 \cong \angle 8$	1. Given
2. $\angle 5$ is complementary to $\angle 6$ and $\angle 7$ is complementary to $\angle 8$.	2. If the exterior sides of a pair of adjacent angles are perpendicular, then the angles are complementary.
3. $\angle 6 \cong \angle 7$	3. If two angles are complementary to congruent angles, then they are congruent.

Problem Set 21

1. True
2. True
3. E
4. A
5. D
6. B
7. B

8. E
9. C
10. A
11. D
12. E
13. $m\angle FOG = 35$
14. $m\angle JOI = 35$
15. 25
16. 141
17. B
18. A
19. C
20. $m\angle XQZ = 72$
21. $AB = 32$
22. Invalid
23. Valid
24.

Statements	Reasons
1. $\overline{FJ} \perp \overline{FG}$, $\overline{GH} \perp \overline{FG}$, $\angle 2 \cong \angle 4$	1. Given
2. $\angle 1$ is complementary to $\angle 2$ and $\angle 3$ is complementary to $\angle 4$.	2. If the exterior sides of a pair of adjacent angles are perpendicular, then the angles are complementary.
3. $\angle 1 \cong \angle 3$	3. If two angles are complementary to congruent angles, then they are congruent.

CHAPTER 4

Practice 22
a. E
b. $m\angle QKE = 80$
c. $m\angle F = 99$
d. $m\angle LKN = 78$
e. A

Problem Set 22
1. True
2. False
3. D
4. A
5. D
6. C
7. E
8. B
9. No; no; no
10. D
11. A
12. C
13. C
14. B
15. A
16. $m\angle LNO = 40$
17. $m\angle KLN = 100$
18. $m\angle ADS = 62$
19. $m\angle J = 116$
20. $GI = 31$
21. $m\angle APC = 86$
22. B
23. E
24. **(1)** Given
(2) Given
(3) $\angle 1 \cong \angle 3$, $\angle 2 \cong \angle 4$
(4) $\angle 1 \cong \angle 2$
(6) Transitive Property
(7) If the exterior sides of adjacent angles are perpendicular, then the angles are complementary.
(8) $\angle 6$ is complementary to $\angle 4$.
(9) $\angle 5 \cong \angle 6$ (If two angles are complementary to congruent angles, then the angles are congruent.)

Practice 23
a. D
b. A
c. $m\angle EFP = 115$
d. $26°, 64°$

e.

Statements	Reasons
1. $\overline{AD} \parallel \overline{BC}$, $\overline{AB} \parallel \overline{DC}$	1. Given
2. $m\angle 6 = m\angle 4$, $m\angle 5 = m\angle 3$	2. If two parallel lines are cut by a transversal, then their alternate interior angles are equal.
3. $m\angle 6 + m\angle 5 = m\angle 4 + m\angle 3$	3. Addition Property
4. $m\angle ABC = m\angle 5 + m\angle 6$ and $m\angle ADC = m\angle 3 + m\angle 4$	4. Betweenness of Rays
5. $m\angle ABC = m\angle ADC$	5. Substitution Property

Problem Set 23
1. True
2. True
3. C
4. D
5. B
6. E
7. A
8. D
9. B
10. C
11. A
12. D
13. $m\angle AOB = 60$
14. $m\angle COQ = 60$
15. $m\angle GOI = 57$
16. $CT = 92$
17. $m\angle AOB = 26$
18. $32°, 58°$
19. 36
20. Valid
21. Invalid
22.

Statements	Reasons
1. $\angle AOB$ and $\angle BOC$ are a linear pair.	1. Given
2. $m\angle AOB + m\angle BOC = 180$	2. If two angles are a linear pair, then they are supplementary.
3. $m\angle AOB = m\angle BOC$	3. Given
4. $m\angle AOB + m\angle AOB = 180$ or $2m\angle AOB = 180$	4. Substitution Property
5. $m\angle AOB = 90$	5. Division Property
6. $m\angle BOC = 90$	6. Substitution Property

7.	$\angle AOB$ and $\angle BOC$ are right angles.	7. Definition of a right angle

23.

	Statements		Reasons
1.	$\overline{DE} \parallel \overline{GF}$, $\overline{EF} \parallel \overline{DG}$	1.	Given
2.	$m\angle 1 = m\angle 4$, $m\angle 2 = m\angle 3$	2.	If two parallel lines are cut by a transversal, then their alternate interior angles are equal.
3.	$m\angle 1 + m\angle 2 = m\angle 4 + m\angle 3$	3.	Addition Property
4.	$m\angle EDG = m\angle 1 + m\angle 2$ and $m\angle EFG = m\angle 3 + m\angle 4$	4.	Betweenness of Rays
5.	$m\angle EDG = m\angle EFG$	5.	Substitution Property

Practice 24
a. C
b. B
c. $m\angle 3 = 35$
d. $m\angle S = 118$

e.

	Statements		Reasons
1.	$\overline{DE} \parallel \overline{FG}$, $\angle D \cong \angle E$	1.	Given
2.	$\angle D$ and $\angle DFG$ are supplementary.	2.	If parallel lines are cut by a transversal, then their interior angles on the same side of the transversal are supplementary.
3.	$\angle E$ and $\angle EGF$ are supplementary.	3.	If parallel lines are cut by a transversal, then their interior angles on the same side of the transversal are supplementary.
4.	$\angle DFG \cong \angle EGF$	4.	If two angles are supplementary to congruent angles, then they are congruent.

Problem Set 24
1. False
2. False
3. A
4. D
5. C
6. E
7. B
8. A
9. A
10. E
11. A
12. C
13. B
14. A
15. $m\angle 2 = 32$
16. $m\angle 3 = 36$
17. $m\angle D = 112$
18. $MN = 14$
19. $m\angle IOJ = 57$
20. 60
21. 69°, 111°

22.

	Statements		Reasons
1.	$\overline{PT} \parallel \overline{WV}$, $\overline{RQ} \parallel \overline{SU}$	1.	Given
2.	$\angle 1 \cong \angle MTW$	2.	If parallel lines are cut by a transversal, then their corresponding angles are congruent.
3.	$\angle 2 \cong \angle MTW$	3.	If parallel lines are cut by a transversal, then their alternate interior angles are congruent.
4.	$\angle 1 \cong \angle 2$	4.	Transitive Property

23.

	Statements		Reasons
1.	$\overline{CP} \parallel \overline{QL}$, $\angle Q \cong \angle L$	1.	Given
2.	$\angle C$ and $\angle Q$ are supplementary.	2.	If parallel lines are cut by a transversal, then their interior angles on the same side of the transversal are supplementary.
3.	$\angle P$ and $\angle L$ are supplementary.	3.	If parallel lines are cut by a transversal, then their interior angles on the same side of the transversal are supplementary.
4.	$\angle C \cong \angle P$	4.	If two angles are supplementary to congruent angles, then they are congruent.

12

Practice 25

a. C
b. $x = 61$
c. $138°$, $42°$
d. Invalid
e.

Statements	Reasons
1. $\overline{GH} \parallel \overline{KL}$; $\overline{IH}$ bisects $\angle GHK$; $\overline{JK}$ bisects $\angle HKL$.	1. Given
2. $m\angle GHI = \frac{1}{2} m\angle GHK$ and $m\angle JKL = \frac{1}{2} m\angle HKL$	2. Definition of an angle bisector
3. $m\angle GHK = m\angle HKL$	3. If parallel lines are cut by a transversal, then their alternate interior angles are congruent.
4. $\frac{1}{2} m\angle GHK = \frac{1}{2} m\angle HKL$	4. Multiplication Property
5. $m\angle GHI = m\angle JKL$	5. Substitution Property

Problem Set 25

1. False
2. True
3. B
4. A
5. D
6. B
7. C
8. A
9. D
10. A
11. C
12. B
13. $x = 67$
14. $m\angle QPR = 90$
15. $m\angle DSE = 41$
16. $KP = 58$
17. $m\angle AOB = 41$
18. $15°$
19. $128°$, $52°$
20. Valid
21. Invalid
22.

Statements	Reasons
1. $\overline{MN} \parallel \overline{PQ} \parallel \overline{SR}$, $\overline{MR} \parallel \overline{ST}$	1. Given
2. $\angle 1 \cong \angle PRS$	2. If parallel lines are cut by a transversal, then their alternate interior angles are congruent.
3. $\angle PRS \cong \angle 2$	3. If parallel lines are cut by a transversal, then their alternate interior angles are congruent.
4. $\angle 1 \cong \angle 2$	4. Transitive Property

23.

Statements	Reasons
1. $\overline{AB} \parallel \overline{FE}$; $\overline{BC}$ bisects $\angle ABE$; $\overline{DE}$ bisects $\angle BEF$.	1. Given
2. $m\angle ABC = \frac{1}{2} m\angle ABE$ and $m\angle DEF = \frac{1}{2} m\angle BEF$	2. Definition of an angle bisector
3. $m\angle ABE = m\angle BEF$	3. If parallel lines are cut by a transversal, then their alternate interior angles are congruent.
4. $\frac{1}{2} m\angle ABE = \frac{1}{2} m\angle BEF$	4. Multiplication Property
5. $m\angle ABC = m\angle DEF$	5. Substitution Property

Practice 26

a. B
b. $x = 51$
c. Invalid
d. A
e.

Statements	Reasons
1. $\angle O \cong \angle U$, $\overline{SO} \parallel \overline{WU}$	1. Given
2. $\angle S \cong \angle U$	2. If two parallel lines are cut by a transversal, then their alternate interior angles are congruent.
3. $\angle O \cong \angle S$	3. Transitive Property
4. $\overline{AO} \parallel \overline{SU}$	4. If two lines form congruent alternate interior angles with a transversal, then the lines are parallel.

Problem Set 26

1. True
2. True

3. C
4. D
5. E
6. B
7. C
8. D
9. A
10. D
11. C
12. B
13. $x = 32$
14. $y = 48$
15. $JP = 82$
16. $m\angle ECF = 48$
17. $m\angle A = 119$
18. Valid
19. Invalid
20. E
21. C

10. C
11. B
12. A
13. B
14. A
15. $x = 25$
16. $y = 22$
17. D
18. A
19. E
20. B
21. $36°$
22. 42
23. (1) $\overline{DE} \perp \overline{EF}$
   (2) $\angle DFE$ is complementary to $\angle DEG$.
   (4) $m\angle DEF = 90$
   (6) Substitution Property
   (7) $m\angle DEG + m\angle FEH = 90$ (Subtraction Property)
   (8) Definition of complementary angles
   (9) $\angle FEH \cong \angle DFE$
   (10) $\overline{DF} \parallel \overline{GH}$ (If two lines form congruent alternate interior angles with a transversal, then the lines are parallel.)

22.

Statements	Reasons
1. $\angle E \cong \angle G$, $\overline{DE} \parallel \overline{FG}$	1. Given
2. $\angle E \cong \angle F$	2. If two parallel lines are cut by a transversal, then their alternate interior angles are congruent.
3. $\angle F \cong \angle G$	3. Transitive Property
4. $\overline{EF} \parallel \overline{GH}$	4. If two lines form congruent alternate interior angles with a transversal, then the lines are parallel.

Practice 27
   a. D
   b. E
   c. $y = 29$
   d. D
   e. 33

Problem Set 27
   1. True
   2. True
   3. C
   4. A
   5. D
   6. D
   7. E
   8. E
   9. B

CHAPTER 5

Practice 28

a. A
b. $m\angle IMN = 70$
c. B
d. $OD = 23$
e.

Statements	Reasons
1. $\angle F \cong \angle S$, $m\angle H + m\angle S = 180$	1. Given
2. $m\angle H + m\angle F = 180$	2. Substitution Property
3. $\overline{FR} \parallel \overline{HS}$	3. If two lines form supplementary interior angles on the same side of a transversal, then the lines are parallel.

Problem Set 28

1. False
2. True
3. D
4. A
5. B
6. B
7. Concave
8. Convex
9. E
10. E
11. C
12. E
13. C
14. B
15. B
16. $m\angle ACB = 82$
17. $m\angle CEF = 68$
18. C
19. A
20. $m\angle WDY = 89$
21. $TR = 49$
22. D
23. D
24.

Statements	Reasons
1. $\angle D \cong \angle L$, $m\angle G + m\angle L = 180$	1. Given
2. $m\angle G + m\angle D = 180$	2. Substitution Property
3. $\overline{DP} \parallel \overline{GL}$	3. If two lines form supplementary interior angles on the same side of a transversal, then the lines are parallel.

Practice 29

a. E
b. C
c. $y = 54$
d. $40°$
e.

Statements	Reasons
1. $d \parallel f$, $f \parallel g$	1. Given
2. $\angle 1 \cong \angle 4$	2. If two parallel lines are cut by a transversal, then their alternate interior angles are congruent.
3. $\angle 4 \cong \angle 8$	3. If two parallel lines are cut by a transversal, then their corresponding angles are congruent.
4. $\angle 1 \cong \angle 8$	4. Transitive Property
5. $d \parallel g$	5. If two lines form congruent alternate interior angles with a transversal, then the lines are parallel.

Problem Set 29

1. True
2. False
3. A
4. C
5. D
6. C
7. E
8. A
9. D
10. C
11. A
12. E
13. C
14. E
15. $x = 30$
16. $y = 51$
17. $36°$
18. 72
19. A
20. A
21. D
22. E
23.

Statements	Reasons
1. $m \parallel n$, $n \parallel q$	1. Given
2. $\angle 2 \cong \angle 3$	2. If two parallel lines are cut by a transversal, then their alternate interior angles are congruent.
3. $\angle 3 \cong \angle 7$	3. If two parallel lines are cut by a transversal, then their corresponding angles are congruent.

4. $\angle 2 \cong \angle 7$ 4. Transitive Property

5. $m \parallel q$ 5. If two lines form congruent alternate interior angles with a transversal, then the lines are parallel.

24.

	Statements		Reasons
1.	$m\angle 1 + m\angle 3 = 180$	1.	Given
2.	$m\angle 1 = m\angle 2$	2.	Pairs of vertical angles are congruent.
3.	$m\angle 2 + m\angle 3 = 180$	3.	Substitution Property
4.	$\angle 2$ and $\angle 3$ are supplementary.	4.	Definition of supplementary angles
5.	$t \parallel r$	5.	If two lines form supplementary interior angles on the same side of a transversal, then the lines are parallel.

Practice 30

a. B
b. E
c. $x = 25$, $y = 80$
d. Valid
e. Statements

	Statements		Reasons
1.	$\overline{AB} \perp \overline{AE}$	1.	Given
2.	$\angle A$ is a right angle.	2.	Definition of perpendicular lines
3.	$\triangle ABE$ is a right triangle.	3.	Definition of right triangle
4.	$\angle B$ and $\angle E$ are complementary.	4.	The acute angles of a right triangle are complementary.
5.	$m\angle B + m\angle E = 90$	5.	Definition of complementary angles

Problem Set 30

1. True
2. True
3. D
4. B
5. C
6. A
7. B
8. A
9. C
10. 30, 60, 90
11. 45, 45, 90

12. C
13. D
14. D
15. A
16. $x = 30$, $y = 75$
17. $x = 40$, $y = 40$
18. $x = 130$, $y = 60$
19. $AC = 19$
20. $m\angle 3 = 35$
21. Valid
22. Invalid

23.

	Statements		Reasons
1.	$\angle C \cong \angle L$	1.	Given
2.	$\angle VBC \cong \angle LBG$	2.	Pairs of vertical angles are congruent.
3.	$\angle V \cong \angle G$	3.	If two angles of a triangle are congruent to two angles of another triangle, then the remaining pair of angles is congruent.

24.

	Statements		Reasons
1.	$\overline{RT} \perp \overline{ST}$	1.	Given
2.	$\angle T$ is a right angle.	2.	Definition of perpendicular lines
3.	$\triangle RST$ is a right triangle.	3.	Definition of a right triangle
4.	$\angle R$ and $\angle S$ are complementary.	4.	The acute angles of a right triangle are complementary.
5.	$m\angle R + m\angle S = 90$	5.	Definition of complementary angles

Practice 31

a. $y = 30$
b. $y = 125$
c. Not possible
d. $72°$
e. Statements

	Statements		Reasons
1.	$\overline{BV} \perp \overline{VG}$, $\overline{GP} \perp \overline{PZ}$	1.	Given
2.	$\angle V$ and $\angle P$ are right angles.	2.	Perpendicular lines intersect to form right angles.
3.	$\angle V \cong \angle P$	3.	All right angles are congruent.
4.	$\angle 3$ and $\angle 4$ are vertical angles.	4.	Given

| 5. | $\angle 3 \cong \angle 4$ | 5. Pairs of vertical angles are congruent. |
| 6. | $\angle B \cong \angle Z$ | 6. If two angles of a triangle are congruent to two angles of another triangle, then the remaining pair of angles are congruent. |

Problem Set 31

1. False
2. True
3. A
4. D
5. D
6. C
7. B
8. 60, 60, 60
9. 10, 80, 90
10. A
11. C
12. B
13. $x = 112$
14. $x = 120$
15. $x = 37$
16. $x = 65$
17. Possible
18. Not possible
19. $69°$
20. $60°$
21. C
22. B
23. Statements — Reasons

Statements	Reasons
1. $\overline{AD} \perp \overline{AF}$, $\overline{FC} \perp \overline{CH}$	1. Given
2. $\angle A$ and $\angle C$ are right angles.	2. Perpendicular lines intersect to form right angles.
3. $\angle A \cong \angle C$	3. All right angles are congruent.
4. $\angle 1$ and $\angle 2$ are vertical angles.	4. Given
5. $\angle 1 \cong \angle 2$	5. Pairs of vertical angles are congruent.
6. $\angle D \cong \angle H$	6. If two angles of a triangle are congruent to two angles of another triangle, then the remaining pair of angles is congruent.

Practice 32

a. D
b. $\overline{YN}$ or $\overline{NY}$
c. $x = 20$, $y = 100$
d. $x = 15$, $y = 136$
e. Statements — Reasons

Statements	Reasons
1. $\angle 4$ is an exterior angle of $\triangle IKL$.	1. Given
2. $m\angle 4 = m\angle L + m\angle 6$	2. Exterior Angle of a Triangle Theorem
3. $m\angle 4 - m\angle 6 = m\angle L$	3. Subtraction Property
4. $m\angle L = m\angle 4 - m\angle 6$	4. Symmetric Property

Problem Set 32

1. True
2. True
3. B
4. B
5. A
6. D
7. D
8. A
9. RPS
10. $\angle P$
11. $\overline{PS}$ or $\overline{SP}$
12. C
13. A
14. B
15. E
16. D
17. $x = 35$, $y = 95$
18. $x = 25$, $y = 105$
19. $x = 23$, $y = 128$
20. $m\angle BOC = 50$
21. $DG = 48$
22. Statements — Reasons

Statements	Reasons
1. $\triangle DFH$ and $\triangle EGI$ are equiangular.	1. Given
2. $m\angle D = 60$ and $m\angle EGI = 60$	2. The measure of each angle of an equiangular triangle is 60.
3. $\angle D \cong \angle EGI$	3. Substitution Property

23. Statements — Reasons

Statements	Reasons
1. $\angle 1$ is an exterior angle of $\triangle URS$.	1. Given
2. $m\angle 1 = m\angle R + m\angle 3$	2. Exterior Angle of a Triangle Theorem
3. $m\angle 1 - m\angle 3 = m\angle R$	3. Subtraction Property

4. $m\angle R = m\angle 1 - m\angle 3$ | 4. Symmetric Property

Practice 33
a. D
b. $m\angle K = 72$, $m\angle JDK = 72$
c. $x = 30$, $y = 120$
d. $36°$
e.

Statements	Reasons
1. $\angle HFG \cong \angle IHF$, J is the midpoint of $\overline{FH}$, $\overline{FG} \cong \overline{HI}$	1. Given
2. $\overline{HJ} \cong \overline{FJ}$	2. Definition of a midpoint
3. $\triangle FGJ \cong \triangle HIJ$	3. Side-Angle-Side

Problem Set 33
1. True
2. True
3. B
4. E
5. D
6. C
7. A
8. C
9. Not possible
10. Possible
11. A
12. C
13. D
14. 38, 52, 90
15. 25, 25, 130
16. $x = 30$, $y = 50$
17. $m\angle S = 60$, $m\angle TRS = 75$
18. $x = 45$, $y = 135$
19. $53°$
20. $45°$
21. E
22. D
23.

Statements	Reasons
1. $\angle BAD \cong \angle ADC$; E is the midpoint of $\overline{AD}$; $\overline{AB} \cong \overline{CD}$	1. Given
2. $\overline{AE} \cong \overline{ED}$	2. Definition of a midpoint
3. $\triangle ABE \cong \triangle DCE$	3. Side-Angle-Side

Practice 34
a. $\overline{BX}$ or $\overline{XB}$
b. B
c. Invalid

d. $x = 30$
e.

Statements	Reasons
1. $\overline{HD} \perp \overline{FH}$, $\overline{FP} \perp \overline{PD}$, $\angle 3 \cong \angle 4$	1. Given
2. $\angle H$ and $\angle P$ are right angles.	2. Perpendicular lines intersect to form right angles.
3. $\angle H \cong \angle P$	3. All right angles are congruent.
4. $\overline{FD} \cong \overline{FD}$	4. Reflexive Property
5. $\triangle HDF \cong \triangle PFD$	5. Angle-Angle-Side

Problem Set 34
1. True
2. False
3. C
4. E
5. E
6. C
7. $\overline{RP}$ or $\overline{PR}$
8. $\angle P$
9. $\overline{LP}$ or $\overline{PL}$
10. $\angle K$
11. A
12. C
13. D
14. D
15. E
16. Valid
17. Invalid
18. $x = 130$
19. $x = 18$
20. $x = 36$
21. $ER = 21$
22. $m\angle A = 134$
23.

Statements	Reasons
1. $\overline{IG} \perp \overline{IK}$, $\overline{GM} \perp \overline{KM}$, $\angle 1 \cong \angle 2$	1. Given
2. $\angle I$ and $\angle M$ are right angles.	2. Perpendicular lines intersect to form right angles.
3. $\angle I \cong \angle M$	3. All right angles are congruent.
4. $\overline{GK} \cong \overline{GK}$	4. Reflexive Property
5. $\triangle GKI \cong \triangle KGM$	5. Angle-Angle-Side

Practice 35
a. C
b. E

18

c. $x = 47$
d. $x = 118$

e.

Statements	Reasons
1. $\overline{NL} \perp \overline{MO}$, $\overline{PQ} \perp \overline{MO}$	1. Given
2. $\angle MLN$ and $\angle OQP$ are right angles.	2. Perpendicular lines intersect to form right angles.
3. $\triangle MLN$ and $\triangle OQP$ are right triangles.	3. Definition of a right triangle
4. $MQ = ML + QL$ and $OL = OQ + QL$	4. Betweenness of Points
5. $MQ = OL$	5. Given
6. $ML + QL = OQ + QL$	6. Substitution Property
7. $ML = OQ$	7. Subtraction Property
8. $MN = PO$	8. Given
9. $\triangle MLN \cong \triangle OQP$	9. Hypotenuse-Leg

Problem Set 35
1. False
2. True
3. E
4. D
5. B
6. B
7. $\overline{TR}$ or $\overline{RT}$
8. $\angle TYR$ or $\angle RYT$
9. $\overline{RY}$ or $\overline{YR}$
10. C
11. E
12. D
13. A
14. C
15. 45, 45, 90
16. C
17. $x = 30$, $y = 30$
18. $x = 40$
19. $x + y = 230$
20. $y = 115$
21. 56
22. 63, 117
23. Statements

Statements	Reasons
1. $\overline{HL} \perp \overline{GI}$, $\overline{JK} \perp \overline{GI}$	1. Given
2. $\angle GLH$ and $\angle IKJ$ are right angles.	2. Perpendicular lines intersect to form right angles.

Statements	Reasons
3. $\triangle GLH$ and $\triangle IKJ$ are right triangles.	3. Definition of a right triangle
4. $GK = GL + LK$ and $LI = IK + LK$	4. Betweenness of Points
5. $GK = LI$	5. Given
6. $GL + LK = IK + LK$	6. Substitution Property
7. $GL = IK$	7. Subtraction Property
8. $GH = JI$	8. Given
9. $\triangle GLH \cong \triangle IKJ$	9. Hypotenuse-Leg

24. **(2)** If two parallel lines are cut by a transversal, then their alternate interior angles are congruent.
(4) Given
(5) Addition Property
(6) Substitution Property
(7) $\overline{VT} \parallel \overline{RS}$
(8) If two parallel lines are cut by a transversal, then their alternate interior angles are congruent.
(9) $\triangle QRS \cong \triangle UVT$ (Angle-Side-Angle)

Practice 36
a. B
b. $x = 4$, $y = 5$
c. $y = 84$
d. $m\angle M = 29$, $m\angle MRE = 61$
e.

Statements	Reasons
1. $\overline{RS} \cong \overline{WU}$, T is the midpoint of $\overline{RW}$	1. Given
2. $\overline{RT} \cong \overline{TW}$	2. Definition of a midpoint
3. $\overline{ST} \cong \overline{TV}$, $\overline{TU} \cong \overline{TV}$	3. Given
4. $\overline{ST} \cong \overline{TU}$	4. Transitive Property
5. $\triangle SRT \cong \triangle UWT$	5. Side-Side-Side

Problem Set 36
1. True
2. True
3. D
4. D
5. A
6. B
7. $\overline{JG}$ or $\overline{GJ}$
8. $\angle J$
9. $\overline{GT}$ or $\overline{TG}$
10. B

11. A
12. D
13. E
14. D
15. $m\angle E = 90$, $m\angle D = 55$, $m\angle F = 35$
16. $x = 2$, $y = 1$
17. $x = 123$
18. $y = 20$
19. $x = 85$
20. $m\angle P = 35$, $m\angle PQC = 55$
21. E
22. D
23.

Statements	Reasons
1. $\overline{AC}$ bisects $\angle BAD$ and $\angle BCD$.	1. Given
2. $\angle BAC \cong \angle DAC$ and $\angle BCA \cong \angle ACD$	2. Definition of an angle bisector
3. $\overline{AC} \cong \overline{AC}$	3. Reflexive Property
4. $\triangle ABC \cong \triangle ADC$	4. Angle-Side-Angle

24.

Statements	Reasons
1. $\overline{LK} \cong \overline{NP}$, M is the midpoint of $\overline{KP}$.	1. Given
2. $\overline{KM} \cong \overline{MP}$	2. Definition of a midpoint
3. $\overline{LM} \cong \overline{OM}$, $\overline{MN} \cong \overline{OM}$	3. Given
4. $\overline{LM} \cong \overline{MN}$	4. Transitive Property
5. $\triangle LKM \cong \triangle NPM$	5. Side-Side-Side

Practice 37
a. $\angle DIY$ or $\angle YID$
b. C
c. $z = 21$
d. 18
e.

Statements	Reasons
1. $\triangle HJD$ is equilateral.	1. Given
2. $\overline{HD} \cong \overline{HJ}$	2. Definition of an equilateral triangle
3. F is the midpoint of $\overline{JD}$.	3. Given
4. $\overline{JF} \cong \overline{FD}$	4. Definition of a midpoint
5. $\overline{HF} \cong \overline{HF}$	5. Reflexive Property
6. $\triangle DFH \cong \triangle JFH$	6. Side-Side-Side

Problem Set 37
1. True
2. False

3. D
4. B
5. B
6. C
7. $\angle U$
8. $\overline{LR}$ or $\overline{RL}$
9. $\angle URL$ or $\angle LRU$
10. $m\overline{NO} = 11$
11. $m\overline{VT} = x$, $m\overline{BT} = x$
12. E
13. A
14. A
15. $x = 75$
16. B
17. $y = 10$
18. $y = 22$
19. $m\angle FEH = 92$
20. $MB = 74$
21. 60
22. 64
23.

Statements	Reasons
1. $\angle A \cong \angle E$, $\overline{AC} \cong \overline{EC}$	1. Given
2. $\angle C \cong \angle C$	2. Reflexive Property
3. $\triangle CAD \cong \triangle CEB$	3. Angle-Side-Angle

24.

Statements	Reasons
1. $\triangle GPK$ is equilateral.	1. Given
2. $\overline{GK} \cong \overline{PK}$	2. Definition of an equilateral triangle
3. L is the midpoint of $\overline{GP}$.	3. Given
4. $\overline{GL} \cong \overline{LP}$	4. Definition of a midpoint
5. $\overline{LK} \cong \overline{LK}$	5. Reflexive Property
6. $\triangle GLK \cong \triangle PLK$	6. Side-Side-Side

CHAPTER 6

Practice 38
a. C
b. D
c. $x = 34$
d. Valid
e. Statements

Statements	Reasons
1. $\overline{UV} \parallel \overline{BW}$, $\overline{AW} \parallel \overline{BV}$	1. Given
2. $\angle UBV \cong \angle BAW$, $\angle U \cong \angle ABW$	2. If two parallel lines are cut by a transversal, then corresponding angles are congruent.
3. $\overline{AW} \cong \overline{BV}$	3. Given
4. $\triangle ABW \cong \triangle BUV$	4. Angle-Angle-Side

Problem Set 38
1. True
2. False
3. B
4. B
5. E
6. 180
7. B
8. C
9. A
10. C
11. D
12. A
13. B
14. B
15. E
16. C
17. $x = 105$, $y = 40$
18. $y = 32$
19. $x = 35$
20. $y = 114$
21. Invalid
22. Valid
23. Statements

Statements	Reasons
1. $\overline{RT} \parallel \overline{PK}$, $\overline{JK} \parallel \overline{PT}$	1. Given
2. $\angle RPT \cong \angle PJK$, $\angle R \cong \angle JPK$	2. If two parallel lines are cut by a transversal, then corresponding angles are congruent.
3. $\overline{JK} \cong \overline{PT}$	3. Given
4. $\triangle JPK \cong \triangle PRT$	4. Angle-Angle-Side

24.
(1) Given
(2) C.P.C.T.C.
(3) Substitution Property
(4) $\overline{BC} \cong \overline{EF}$, $\overline{LM} \cong \overline{EF}$
(5) Substitution Property
(6) C.P.C.T.C.
(7) $\overline{AC} \cong \overline{KM}$
(8) Side-Side-Side

Practice 39
a. E
b. D
c. B
d. C
e. Statements

Statements	Reasons
1. $\overline{AB} \perp \overline{AE}$, $\overline{ED} \perp \overline{AE}$	1. Given
2. $\angle BAC$ and $\angle DEC$ are right angles.	2. Perpendicular lines intersect to form right angles.
3. $\angle BAC \cong \angle DEC$	3. All right angles are congruent.
4. $\angle B \cong \angle D$, $\overline{BC} \cong \overline{CD}$	4. Given
5. $\triangle BAC \cong \triangle DEC$	5. Angle-Angle-Side
6. $\overline{AC} \cong \overline{EC}$	6. C.P.C.T.C.
7. C is the midpoint of $\overline{AE}$.	7. Definition of a midpoint

Problem Set 39
1. True
2. True
3. D
4. A
5. A
6. D
7. $\overline{CH}$ or $\overline{HC}$
8. $\angle QHD$ or $\angle DHQ$
9. $\overline{HQ}$ or $\overline{QH}$
10. $\angle CHQ$ or $\angle QHC$
11. D
12. E
13. A
14. B
15. A
16. C
17. $y = 26$
18. $x = 35$
19. $x = 37$
20. A
21. 135

22. 15

23.

Statements	Reasons
1. $\overline{AO} \cong \overline{CO}$, $\overline{AB} \cong \overline{CB}$	1. Given
2. $\overline{BO} \cong \overline{BO}$	2. Reflexive Property
3. $\triangle ABO \cong \triangle CBO$	3. Side-Side-Side
4. $\angle ABO \cong \angle CBO$	4. C.P.C.T.C.
5. $\overline{BO}$ bisects $\angle ABC$.	5. Definition of an angle bisector

24.

Statements	Reasons
1. $\overline{FD} \perp \overline{DH}$, $\overline{JH} \perp \overline{DH}$	1. Given
2. $\angle FDG$ and $\angle JHG$ are right angles.	2. Perpendicular lines intersect to form right angles.
3. $\angle FDG \cong \angle JHG$	3. All right angles are congruent.
4. $\angle F \cong \angle J$, $\overline{FG} \cong \overline{JG}$	4. Given
5. $\triangle FDG \cong \triangle JHG$	5. Angle-Angle-Side
6. $\overline{DG} \cong \overline{HG}$	6. C.P.C.T.C.
7. G is the midpoint of $\overline{DH}$.	7. Definition of a midpoint

Practice 40

a. A

b. C

c. $x = 9$, $y = 29$

d. $x = 17$, $y = 16$

e.

Statements	Reasons
1. $\overline{JG} \parallel \overline{KM}$, $\overline{JG} \cong \overline{KM}$, $\overline{HJ} \cong \overline{JK}$	1. Given
2. $\angle HJG \cong \angle JKM$	2. If two parallel lines are cut by a transversal, then corresponding angles are congruent.
3. $\triangle GHJ \cong MJK$	3. Side-Angle-Side
4. $\angle H \cong \angle KJM$	4. C.P.C.T.C.
5. $\overline{HG} \parallel \overline{JM}$	5. If two lines form congruent corresponding angles with a transversal, then the lines are parallel.

Problem Set 40

1. True

2. True

3. C

4. D

5. C

6. E

7. B

8. A

9. D

10. E

11. B

12. B

13. C

14. C

15. A

16. $x = 142$

17. $x = 13$, $y = 55$

18. $x = 39$, $y = 88$

19. $x = 14$, $y = 19$

20. D

21. B

22.

Statements	Reasons
1. $\overline{MT} \cong \overline{LT}$, $\overline{OT}$ is a bisector of $\angle MTL$.	1. Given
2. $\angle MTO \cong \angle LTO$	2. Definition of an angle bisector
3. $\overline{OT} \cong \overline{OT}$	3. Reflexive Property
4. $\triangle MTO \cong \triangle LTO$	4. Side-Angle-Side
5. $\angle MOT \cong \angle LOT$	5. C.P.C.T.C.
6. $\angle MOT$ and $\angle LOT$ are a linear pair.	6. Definition of a linear pair
7. $\angle MOT$ and $\angle LOT$ are right angles.	7. If two angles in a linear pair are congruent, then each is a right angle.
8. $\overline{OT} \perp \overline{LM}$	8. Definition of perpendicular lines

23.

Statements	Reasons
1. $\overline{BE} \parallel \overline{CD}$, $\overline{BE} \cong \overline{CD}$, $\overline{AE} \cong \overline{ED}$	1. Given
2. $\angle BEA \cong \angle CDE$	2. If two parallel lines are cut by a transversal, then corresponding angles are congruent.
3. $\triangle ABE \cong \triangle ECD$	3. Side-Angle-Side
4. $\angle A \cong \angle CED$	4. C.P.C.T.C.
5. $\overline{AB} \parallel \overline{CE}$	5. If two lines form congruent corresponding angles with a transversal, then the lines are parallel.

Practice 41

a. B
b. A
c. $x = 56$, $y = 28$, $z = 64$
d. 30, 150
e.

Statements	Reasons
1. $\overline{MF}$ is the perpendicular bisector of $\overline{DE}$.	1. Given
2. $\overline{MF} \perp \overline{DE}$, $\overline{DM} \cong \overline{ME}$	2. Definition of a perpendicular bisector
3. $\angle DMF$ and $\angle EMF$ are right angles.	3. Perpendicular lines intersect to form right angles.
4. $\angle DMF \cong \angle EMF$	4. All right angles are congruent.
5. $\overline{MF} \cong \overline{MF}$	5. Reflexive Property
6. $\triangle FDM \cong \triangle FEM$	6. Side-Angle-Side
7. $\overline{FD} \cong \overline{FE}$	7. C.P.C.T.C.

Problem Set 41

1. False
2. False
3. C
4. A
5. D
6. C
7. A
8. B
9. E
10. C
11. D
12. E
13. A
14. E
15. $x = 125$, $y = 75$
16. $x = 58$, $y = 29$, $z = 60$
17. $x = 47$, $y = 27$
18. $x = 59$, $y = 31$
19. Valid
20. Invalid
21. 30, 60
22. 80, 100
23.

Statements	Reasons
1. $\overline{BX}$ is the perpendicular bisector of $\overline{AC}$.	1. Given
2. $\overline{BX} \perp \overline{AC}$, $\overline{AX} \cong \overline{XC}$	2. Definition of a perpendicular bisector
3. $\angle BXC$ and $\angle BXA$ are right angles.	3. Perpendicular lines intersect to form right angles.
4. $\angle BXC \cong \angle BXA$	4. All right angles are congruent.
5. $\overline{BX} \cong \overline{BX}$	5. Reflexive Property
6. $\triangle ABX \cong \triangle CBX$	6. Side-Angle-Side
7. $\overline{AB} \cong \overline{BC}$	7. C.P.C.T.C.

24. (3) Reflexive Property
(4) Side-Side-Side
(5) $\angle BXA \cong \angle BXC$
(6) Definition of a linear pair
(7) If the two angles in a linear pair are congruent, then each is a right angle.
(8) $\overline{BX} \perp \overline{AC}$

Practice 42

a. D
b. 40, 70, 70
c. $y = 84$
d. $y = 30$
e.

Statements	Reasons
1. $\overline{PN} \cong \overline{PK}$, $\overline{NM} \cong \overline{LK}$	1. Given
2. $\angle N \cong \angle K$	2. Base Angles Theorem
3. $\angle 3 \cong \angle 4$	3. Given
4. $\angle NOM$ and $\angle 3$ are a linear pair; $\angle LQK$ and $\angle 4$ are a linear pair.	4. Definition of a linear pair
5. $\angle NOM$ and $\angle 3$ are supplementary; $\angle LQK$ and $\angle 4$ are supplementary.	5. If two angles are a linear pair, then they are supplementary.
6. $\angle NOM \cong \angle LQK$	6. If two angles are supplementary to congruent angles, then they are congruent.
7. $\triangle NMO \cong \triangle KLQ$	7. Angle-Angle-Side
8. $\overline{MO} \cong \overline{LQ}$	8. C.P.C.T.C.

Problem Set 42

1. True
2. True
3. E
4. B
5. A

6. A
7. $\angle ECF$ or $\angle FCE$
8. $\overline{FE}$ or $\overline{EF}$
9. $\triangle CEB$
10. E
11. 50, 65, 65
12. C
13. A
14. D
15. B
16. E
17. $x = 72$
18. $x = 76$
19. $x = 65$, $y = 64$
20. $y = 48$
21. E
22. A

23.

Statements	Reasons
1. $\triangle PEG$, $\overline{EP} \cong \overline{EG}$, altitudes $\overline{PK}$ and $\overline{GH}$	1. Given
2. $\angle PHG$ and $\angle GKP$ are right angles.	2. Definition of an altitude
3. $\angle PHG \cong \angle GKP$	3. All right angles are congruent.
4. $\angle HPG \cong \angle KGP$	4. Base Angles Theorem
5. $\overline{PG} \cong \overline{PG}$	5. Reflexive Property
6. $\triangle PHG \cong \triangle GKP$	6. Angle-Angle-Side
7. $\overline{PK} \cong \overline{GH}$	7. C.P.C.T.C.

24.

Statements	Reasons
1. $\overline{DF} \cong \overline{AF}$, $\overline{DC} \cong \overline{AB}$	1. Given
2. $\angle A \cong \angle D$	2. Base Angles Theorem
3. $\angle 1 \cong \angle 2$	3. Given
4. $\angle DEC$ and $\angle 1$ are a linear pair; $\angle BGA$ and $\angle 2$ are a linear pair.	4. Definition of a linear pair
5. $\angle DEC$ and $\angle 1$ are supplementary; $\angle BGA$ and $\angle 2$ are supplementary.	5. If two angles are a linear pair, then they are supplementary.
6. $\angle DEC \cong \angle BGA$	6. If two angles are supplementary to congruent angles, then they are congruent.
7. $\triangle ABG \cong \triangle DCE$	7. Angle-Angle-Side

8.

8. $\overline{CE} \cong \overline{BG}$	8. C.P.C.T.C.

Practice 43

a. C
b. $z = 7$
c. $x = 8$
d. 126, 54
e.

Statements	Reasons
1. $\overline{AB} \cong \overline{BC}$; $\overline{JC}$ and $\overline{KA}$ are medians of $\triangle ABC$.	1. Given
2. J is the midpoint of $\overline{AB}$ and K is the midpoint of $\overline{BC}$.	2. Definition of a median
3. $AJ = \frac{1}{2}AB$ and $KC = \frac{1}{2}BC$	3. Definition of a midpoint
4. $\frac{1}{2}AB = \frac{1}{2}BC$	4. Multiplication Property
5. $AJ = KC$ or $\overline{AJ} \cong \overline{KC}$	5. Substitution Property
6. $\angle BAC \cong \angle BCA$	6. Base Angles Theorem
7. $\overline{AC} \cong \overline{AC}$	7. Reflexive Property
8. $\triangle JAC \cong \triangle KCA$	8. Side-Angle-Side
9. $\overline{JC} \cong \overline{KA}$	9. C.P.C.T.C.

Problem Set 43

1. True
2. True
3. 60
4. A
5. D
6. $\angle PDE$ or $\angle EDP$
7. A
8. $\overline{ED}$ or $\overline{DE}$
9. A
10. D
11. C
12. C
13. E
14. B
15. $x = 15$, $y = 60$
16. $x = 35$, $y = 20$
17. $y = 6$
18. $x = 5$
19. 72
20. 114, 66

21. B

22. D

23.

Statements	Reasons
1. $\overline{WT} \cong \overline{TU}$; $\overline{RU}$ and $\overline{SW}$ are medians of $\triangle WTU$.	1. Given
2. R is the midpoint of $\overline{TW}$ and S is the midpoint of $\overline{TU}$.	2. Definition of a median
3. $RW = \frac{1}{2}WT$ and $US = \frac{1}{2}TU$	3. Definition of a midpoint
4. $\frac{1}{2}WT = \frac{1}{2}TU$	4. Multiplication Property
5. $RW = US$ or $\overline{RW} \cong \overline{US}$	5. Substitution Property
6. $\angle TWU \cong \angle TUW$	6. Base Angles Theorem
7. $\overline{WU} \cong \overline{WU}$	7. Reflexive Property
8. $\triangle RWU \cong \triangle SUW$	8. Size-Angle-Side
9. $\overline{RU} \cong \overline{SW}$	9. C.P.C.T.C.

24.

Statements	Reasons
1. $\overline{PS} \cong \overline{QS}$	1. Given
2. $\angle 2 \cong \angle 3$	2. Base Angles Theorem
3. $\angle 1$, $\angle 2$ and $\angle 3$, $\angle 4$ are linear pairs.	3. Definition of a linear pair
4. $\angle 1$, $\angle 2$ and $\angle 3$, $\angle 4$ are supplementary.	4. If two angles are a linear pair, then they are supplementary.
5. $\angle 1 \cong \angle 4$	5. If two angles are supplementary to congruent angles, then they are congruent.
6. $\overline{DP} \cong \overline{LQ}$	6. Given
7. $\triangle DPS \cong \triangle LQS$	7. Side-Angle-Side
8. $\overline{DS} \cong \overline{LS}$	8. C.P.C.T.C.
9. $\triangle DSL$ is isosceles.	9. Definition of an isosceles triangle

CHAPTER 7

Practice 44

a. >
b. C
c. B
d. $z = 30$
e. Statements | Reasons

	Statements		Reasons
1.	$\overline{FB} \perp \overline{AC}$, $\overline{FE} \perp \overline{AD}$	1.	Given
2.	$\angle DEF$ and $\angle CBF$ are right angles.	2.	Perpendicular lines intersect to form right angles.
3.	$\triangle DEF$ and $\triangle CBF$ are right triangles.	3.	Definition of a right triangle
4.	$\overline{FB} \cong \overline{FE}$, F is the midpoint of $\overline{CD}$.	4.	Given
5.	$\overline{DF} \cong \overline{CF}$	5.	Definition of a midpoint
6.	$\triangle DEF \cong \triangle CBF$	6.	Hypotenuse-Leg
7.	$\angle D \cong \angle C$	7.	C.P.C.T.C.
8.	$\overline{AD} \cong \overline{AC}$	8.	Converse of the Base Angles Theorem
9.	$\triangle CAD$ is isosceles.	9.	Definition of an isosceles triangle

Problem Set 44

1. False
2. True
3. C
4. D
5. B
6. E
7. <
8. >
9. <
10. D
11. C
12. E
13. 110, 35, 35
14. A
15. A
16. A
17. E
18. D
19. $x = 41$
20. $y = 21$
21. $x = 82$, $y = 15$
22. $x = 126$, $y = 54$

23. Statements | Reasons

	Statements		Reasons
1.	$\angle D \cong \angle H$, $\overline{DF} \cong \overline{HF}$	1.	Given
2.	$\angle F \cong \angle F$	2.	Reflexive Property
3.	$\triangle DGF \cong \triangle HEF$	3.	Angle-Side-Angle
4.	$\overline{DG} \cong \overline{HE}$	4.	C.P.C.T.C.

24. Statements | Reasons

	Statements		Reasons
1.	$\overline{YS} \perp \overline{RT}$, $\overline{YU} \perp \overline{RV}$	1.	Given
2.	$\angle VUY$ and $\angle TSY$ are right angles.	2.	Perpendicular lines intersect to form right angles.
3.	$\triangle VUY$ and $\triangle TSY$ are right triangles.	3.	Definition of a right triangle
4.	$\overline{YS} \cong \overline{YU}$, Y is the midpoint of $\overline{TV}$.	4.	Given
5.	$\overline{VY} \cong \overline{TY}$	5.	Definition of a midpoint
6.	$\triangle VUY \cong \triangle TSY$	6.	Hypotenuse-Leg
7.	$\angle V \cong \angle T$	7.	C.P.C.T.C.
8.	$\overline{RV} \cong \overline{RT}$	8.	Converse of the Base Angles Theorem
9.	$\triangle TRV$ is isosceles.	9.	Definition of an isosceles triangle

Practice 45

a. Yes
b. A
c. $x = 52$
d. 140, 40
e. Statements | Reasons

	Statements		Reasons
1.	$\overline{TR} \cong \overline{TS}$, $\overline{AT}$ bisects $\angle RTS$.	1.	Given
2.	$\angle RTU \cong \angle STU$	2.	Definition of an angle bisector
3.	$\overline{TU} \cong \overline{TU}$	3.	Reflexive Property
4.	$\triangle RTU \cong \triangle STU$	4.	Side-Angle-Side
5.	$\overline{RU} \cong \overline{SU}$	5.	C.P.C.T.C.
6.	$\angle RUT \cong \angle SUT$	6.	C.P.C.T.C.
7.	$\angle RUT$ and $\angle RUA$ are supplementary; $\angle SUT$ and $\angle SUA$ are supplementary.	7.	If two angles are a linear pair, then they are supplementary.
8.	$\angle RUA \cong \angle SUA$	8.	If two angles are supplementary to congruent angles,

9.	$\overline{UA} \cong \overline{UA}$	9.	Reflexive Property
10.	$\triangle RUA \cong \triangle SUA$	10.	Side-Angle-Side

Problem Set 45

1. True
2. False
3. B
4. B
5. E
6. >
7. <
8. A
9. D
10. Yes
11. No
12. Yes
13. A
14. C
15. B
16. D
17. $x = 66$
18. $y = 46$
19. $x = 40$, $y = 40$
20. $x = 15$, $y = 20$
21. 56
22. 163, 17

23. Statements | **Reasons**

	Statements		Reasons
1.	$\overline{EA} \cong \overline{EU}$	1.	Given
2.	$\angle 1 \cong \angle 3$	2.	Base Angles Theorem
3.	$\overline{AU} \parallel \overline{IO}$	3.	Given
4.	$\angle 1 \cong \angle 2$ and $\angle 3 \cong \angle 4$	4.	If two parallel lines are cut by a transversal, then corresponding angles are congruent.
5.	$\angle 2 \cong \angle 3$	5.	Transitive Property
6.	$\angle 2 \cong \angle 4$	6.	Transitive Property
7.	$\overline{IE} \cong \overline{OE}$	7.	Converse of the Base Angles Theorem
8.	$\triangle IEO$ is isosceles.	8.	Definition of an isosceles triangle

24. Statements | **Reasons**

	Statements		Reasons
1.	$\overline{FG} \cong \overline{FH}$, $\overline{FK}$ bisects $\angle HFG$.	1.	Given

2.	$\angle GFJ \cong \angle HFJ$	2.	Definition of an angle bisector
3.	$\overline{FJ} \cong \overline{FJ}$	3.	Reflexive Property
4.	$\triangle GFJ \cong \triangle HFJ$	4.	Side-Angle-Side
5.	$\overline{GJ} \cong \overline{HJ}$	5.	C.P.C.T.C.
6.	$\angle GJF \cong \angle HJF$	6.	C.P.C.T.C.
7.	$\angle GJF$ and $\angle GJK$ are supplementary; $\angle HJF$ and $\angle HJK$ are supplementary.	7.	If two angles are a linear pair, then they are supplementary.
8.	$\angle GJK \cong \angle HJK$	8.	If two angles are supplementary to congruent angles, then they are congruent.
9.	$\overline{JK} \cong \overline{JK}$	9.	Reflexive Property
10.	$\triangle GJK \cong \triangle HJK$	10.	Side-Angle-Side

Practice 46

a. C
b. $x = 70$, $y = 35$
c. $y = 72$
d. $ST = 13$, $TU = 13$
e. **Statements** | **Reasons**

	Statements		Reasons
1.	$\overline{GH} \parallel \overline{IJ}$, $\overline{GH} \cong \overline{IJ}$, $\overline{GK} \cong \overline{IL}$	1.	Given
2.	$\angle HGK \cong \angle JIL$	2.	If two parallel lines are cut by a transversal, then their alternate interior angles are congruent.
3.	$\triangle HGK \cong \triangle JIL$	3.	Side-Angle-Side
4.	$\overline{HK} \cong \overline{JL}$	4.	C.P.C.T.C.
5.	$GK = IL$	5.	Congruent segments have equal lengths.
6.	$GK + KL = IL + LK$	6.	Addition Property
7.	$GK + KL = GL$ and $IL + LK = IK$	7.	Betweenness of Points
8.	$GL = IK$ or $\overline{GL} \cong \overline{IK}$	8.	Substitution Property
9.	$\angle HKG \cong \angle JLI$	9.	C.P.C.T.C.
10.	$\angle HKG$ and $\angle HKI$ are supplementary; $\angle JLI$ and $\angle JLG$ are supplementary.	10.	If two angles are a linear pair, then they are supplementary.

11.	$\angle HKI \cong \angle JLG$	11. If two angles are supplementary to congruent angles, then they are congruent.
12.	$\triangle HKI \cong \triangle JLG$	12. Side-Angle-Side
13.	$\angle IHK \cong \angle GJL$	13. C.P.C.T.C.

Problem Set 46

1. True
2. True
3. A
4. C
5. A
6. A
7. C
8. No
9. Yes
10. 20, 20, 140
11. 90, 45, 45
12. B
13. B
14. D
15. $x = 65$, $y = 105$
16. $x = 50$, $y = 20$
17. $x = 40$, $y = 50$
18. $x = 15$, $y = 75$
19. $m\angle H = 19$, $m\angle K = 71$
20. $DE = 11$, $EF = 11$
21. Invalid
22. Valid

23.

	Statements		Reasons
1.	$\overline{BA} \perp \overline{PA}$, $\overline{CD} \perp \overline{PD}$	1.	Given
2.	$\angle BAP$ and $\angle CDP$ are right angles.	2.	Perpendicular lines intersect to form right angles.
3.	$\angle BAP \cong \angle CDP$	3.	All right angles are congruent.
4.	$\angle APB \cong \angle DPC$	4.	Pairs of vertical angles are congruent.
5.	Point P is the midpoint of $\overline{BC}$.	5.	Given
6.	$\overline{BP} \cong \overline{CP}$	6.	Definition of a midpoint
7.	$\triangle BAP \cong \triangle CDP$	7.	Angle-Angle-Side
8.	$\overline{AP} \cong \overline{DP}$	8.	C.P.C.T.C.
9.	$\overline{BC}$ bisects $\overline{AD}$.	9.	Definition of a segment bisector

24.

	Statements		Reasons
1.	$\overline{AB} \parallel \overline{CD}$, $\overline{AB} \cong \overline{CD}$, $\overline{AE} \cong \overline{CF}$	1.	Given
2.	$\angle BAE \cong \angle DCF$	2.	If two parallel lines are cut by a transversal, then their alternate interior angles are congruent.
3.	$\triangle BAE \cong \triangle DCF$	3.	Side-Angle-Side
4.	$\overline{BE} \cong \overline{DF}$	4.	C.P.C.T.C.
5.	$AE = CF$	5.	Congruent segments have equal lengths.
6.	$AE + EF = CF + EF$	6.	Addition Property
7.	$AE + EF = AF$ and $CF + EF = CE$	7.	Betweenness of Points
8.	$AF = CE$ or $\overline{AF} \cong \overline{CE}$	8.	Substitution Property
9.	$\angle BEA \cong \angle DFC$	9.	C.P.C.T.C.
10.	$\angle BEA$ and $\angle BEC$ are supplementary; $\angle DFC$ and $\angle DFA$ are supplementary.	10.	If two angles are a linear pair, then they are supplementary.
11.	$\angle BEC \cong \angle DFA$	11.	If two angles are supplementary to congruent angles, then they are congruent.
12.	$\triangle BEC \cong \triangle DFA$	12.	Side-Angle-Side
13.	$\angle CBE \cong \angle ADF$	13.	C.P.C.T.C.

Practice 47

a. Greater than 4 and less than 16
b. C
c. B
d. 40, 140
e.

	Statements		Reasons
1.	$\overline{KM} \perp \overline{NL}$, $\angle 3$ is not $\cong$ to $\angle 4$.	1.	Given
2.	Either $\overline{KM}$ is not the median to side $\overline{NL}$ or $\overline{KM}$ is the median to side $\overline{NL}$. Assume $\overline{KM}$ is the median to side $\overline{NL}$.	2.	A statement is either true or false.
3.	$\overline{NM} \cong \overline{ML}$	3.	Definition of a median

4.	∠KMN and ∠KML are right angles.	4.	Perpendicular lines intersect to form right angles.
5.	∠KMN ≅ ∠KML	5.	All right angles are congruent.
6.	$\overline{KM} ≅ \overline{KM}$	6.	Reflexive Property
7.	ΔKMN ≅ ΔKML	7.	Side-Angle-Side
8.	∠3 ≅ ∠4	8.	C.P.C.T.C.
9.	$\overline{KM}$ is not the median to side $\overline{NL}$.	9.	Statement 8 contradicts the given statement that ∠3 is not ≅ to ∠4. The assumption made in statement 2 must be false. By elimination, statement 9 must be true.

Problem Set 47

1. True
2. False
3. D
4. A
5. D
6. Greater than 2 and less than 28
7. Greater than 13 and less than 23
8. B
9. A
10. E
11. B
12. C
13. E
14. A
15. $x = 13$, $y = 11$
16. B
17. $y = 47$
18. A
19. 32, 58
20. 108, 72
21. C
22. E
23.

	Statements		Reasons
1.	$\overline{EF} ≅ \overline{GF}$	1.	Given
2.	$m∠1 = m∠2$	2.	Base Angles Theorem
3.	$m∠3 > m∠2$	3.	Exterior Angle Inequality Theorem
4.	$m∠3 > m∠1$	4.	Substitution Property

24.

	Statements		Reasons
1.	$\overline{DB} ⊥ \overline{AC}$, ∠1 is not ≅ to ∠2.	1.	Given
2.	Either $\overline{DB}$ is not the median to side $\overline{AC}$ or $\overline{DB}$ is the median to side $\overline{AC}$. Assume $\overline{DB}$ is the median to side $\overline{AC}$.	2.	A statement is either true or false.
3.	$\overline{AB} ≅ \overline{BC}$	3.	Definition of a median
4.	∠DBA and ∠DBC are right angles.	4.	Perpendicular lines intersect to form right angles.
5.	∠DBA ≅ ∠DBC	5.	All right angles are congruent.
6.	$\overline{DB} ≅ \overline{DB}$	6.	Reflexive Property
7.	ΔDBA ≅ ΔDBC	7.	Side-Angle-Side
8.	∠1 ≅ ∠2	8.	C.P.C.T.C.
9.	$\overline{DB}$ is not the median to side $\overline{AC}$.	9.	Statement 8 contradicts the given statement that ∠1 is not ≅ to ∠2. The assumption made in statement 2 must be false. By elimination, statement 9 must be true.

Practice 48

a. C
b. Converse: False
   Inverse: False
   Contrapositive: True
c. $a + b = 135$
d. $a = 54$
e.

	Statements		Reasons
1.	∠3 ≅ ∠4	1.	Given
2.	Either $KL = JK$ or $KL ≠ JK$. Assume $KL = JK$.	2.	A statement is either true or false.
3.	∠4 ≅ ∠J	3.	Base Angles Theorem
4.	∠3 ≅ ∠J	4.	Transitive Property
5.	$KL ≠ JK$	5.	Statement 4 contradicts the Exterior Angle Inequality Theorem. The assumption made in statement 2 must be

false. By elimination, statement 5 must be true.

By elimination, statement 5 must be true.

Problem Set 48
1. True
2. True
3. D
4. B
5. A
6. C
7. Greater than 3 and less than 5
8. Greater than 10 and less than 28
9. B
10. A
11. C
12. Converse: False
    Inverse: False
    Contrapositive: True
13. Converse: False
    Inverse: False
    Contrapositive: True
14. A
15. 15, 75, 90
16. C
17. E
18. A
19. $w + x + y + z = 300$
20. $s + t = 130$
21. B
22. $b = 40$

23.

Statements	Reasons
1. G is between H and E.	1. Given
2. $m\angle HGD > m\angle GED$	2. Exterior Angle Inequality Theorem
3. $m\angle GED > m\angle F$	3. Exterior Angle Inequality Theorem
4. $m\angle HGD > m\angle F$	4. Transitive Property of Inequality

24.

Statements	Reasons
1. $\angle 1 \cong \angle 2$	1. Given
2. Either $RS = ST$ or $RS \neq ST$. Assume $RS = ST$.	2. A statement is either true or false.
3. $\angle 2 \cong \angle T$	3. Base Angles Theorem
4. $\angle 1 \cong \angle T$	4. Transitive Property
5. $RS \neq ST$	5. Statement 4 contradicts the Exterior Angle Inequality Theorem. The assumption made in statement 2 must be false.

Practice 49
a. B
b. Converse: True
   Inverse: True
   Contrapositive: False
c. $\overline{JQ}$ or $\overline{QJ}$
d. A
e.

Statements	Reasons
1. $KN = PN$	1. Given
2. Either $PM = MO$ or $PM \neq MO$. Assume $PM = MO$.	2. A statement is either true or false.
3. $m\angle 3 = m\angle 4$	3. Base Angles Theorem
4. $m\angle 4 > m\angle K$	4. Exterior Angle Inequality Theorem
5. $m\angle 3 > m\angle K$	5. Substitution Property of Inequality
6. $m\angle NPK > m\angle 3$	6. Whole Greater Than Its Part Property
7. $m\angle NPK > m\angle K$	7. Transitive Property of Inequality
8. $KN > PN$	8. If Unequal Angles, then Unequal Sides
9. $PM \neq MO$	9. Statement 8 contradicts the given statement that $KN = PN$. The assumption made in statement 2 must be false. By elimination, statement 9 must be true.

Problem Set 49
1. True
2. True
3. D
4. B
5. C
6. A
7. C
8. A
9. B
10. Converse: True
    Inverse: True
    Contrapositive: False

11. Converse: True
    Inverse: True
    Contrapositive: False
12. $\angle A$
13. $\overline{DF}$ or $\overline{FD}$
14. C
15. E
16. A
17. A
18. D
19. $p + q = 146$
20. $m\angle NRT = 109$
21. E
22. $x = 34$

23.

Statements	Reasons
1. $m\angle 5 = m\angle 6$	1. Given
2. $m\angle 5 > m\angle C$	2. Exterior Angle Inequality Theorem
3. $m\angle 6 > m\angle C$	3. Substitution Property of Inequality
4. $EC > AE$	4. If Unequal Angles, Then Unequal Sides

24.

Statements	Reasons
1. $AB = CB$	1. Given
2. Either $AD = DE$ or $AD \neq DE$. Assume $AD = DE$.	2. A statement is either true or false.
3. $m\angle 1 = m\angle 2$	3. Base Angles Theorem
4. $m\angle 2 > m\angle C$	4. Exterior Angle Inequality Theorem
5. $m\angle 1 > m\angle C$	5. Substitution Property of Inequality
6. $m\angle BAC > m\angle 1$	6. Whole Greater Than Its Part Property
7. $m\angle BAC > m\angle C$	7. Transitive Property of Inequality
8. $AB < CB$	8. If Unequal Angles, then Unequal Sides
9. $AD \neq DE$	9. Statement 8 contradicts the given statement that $AB = CB$. The assumption made in statement 2 must be false. By elimination, statement 9 must be true.

31

CHAPTER 8

Practice 50
a. B
b. Converse: True
   Inverse: True
   Contrapositive: True
c. $\angle J$
d. $x = 73$
e. Statements / Reasons

Statements	Reasons
1. $\triangle ABC$ is equilateral; point Q is any point on $\overline{AB}$.	1. Given
2. $m\angle CQA > m\angle B$	2. Exterior Angle Inequality Theorem
3. $m\angle A = m\angle B$	3. If a triangle is equilateral, then it is equiangular.
4. $m\angle CQA > m\angle A$	4. Substitution Property of Inequality
5. $CQ < AC$	5. If Unequal Angles, then Unequal Sides
6. $AC = CB = AB$	6. Definition of an equilateral triangle
7. $CQ < BC$ and $CQ < AB$	7. Substitution Property of Inequality

Problem Set 50
1. True
2. False
3. A
4. E
5. E
6. C
7. D
8. E
9. Greater than 9 and less than 19
10. Greater than 20 and less than 110
11. C
12. B
13. Converse: True
    Inverse: True
    Contrapositive: True
14. Converse: False
    Inverse: False
    Contrapositive: True
15. $\overline{BC}$ or $\overline{CB}$
16. $\angle R$
17. D
18. C
19. $x = 70$
20. $y = 76$
21. $m\angle B = 40$, $m\angle C = 20$
22. 135, 45

23. Statements / Reasons

Statements	Reasons
1. $EU = UT$	1. Given
2. $m\angle 1 = m\angle 2$	2. Base Angles Theorem
3. $m\angle 3 > m\angle 2$	3. Exterior Angle Inequality Theorem
4. $m\angle 3 > m\angle 1$	4. Substitution Property of Inequality
5. $EU > UR$	5. If Unequal Angles, then Unequal Sides

24. Statements / Reasons

Statements	Reasons
1. $\triangle JKL$ is equilateral; point P is any point on $\overline{JL}$.	1. Given
2. $m\angle KPJ > m\angle L$	2. Exterior Angle Inequality Theorem
3. $m\angle J = m\angle L$	3. If a triangle is equilateral, then it is equiangular.
4. $m\angle KPJ > m\angle J$	4. Substitution Property of Inequality
5. $KP < JK$	5. If Unequal Angles, then Unequal Sides
6. $JK = KL = JL$	6. Definition of an equilateral triangle
7. $KP < KL$ and $KP < JL$	7. Substitution Property of Inequality

Practice 51
a. A
b. C
c. Converse: True
   Inverse: True
   Contrapositive: True
d. $y = 75$
e. Statements / Reasons

Statements	Reasons
1. $FGHJ$ is an isosceles trapezoid with $\overline{FJ} \cong \overline{GH}$.	1. Given
2. $\angle JFG \cong \angle HGF$	2. The base angles of an isosceles trapezoid are congruent.
3. $\overline{FG} \cong \overline{FG}$	3. Reflexive Property
4. $\triangle FHG \cong \triangle GJF$	4. Side-Angle-Side
5. $\overline{FH} \cong \overline{GJ}$	5. C.P.C.T.C.

Problem Set 51
1. False
2. True
3. B
4. C
5. C
6. B
7. A
8. C
9. B
10. E
11. Converse: True
    Inverse: True
    Contrapositive: True
12. Converse: True
    Inverse: True
    Contrapositive: True
13. $\angle R$
14. $\overline{AC}$ or $\overline{CA}$
15. $\angle F$
16. E
17. D
18. C
19. $y = 40$
20. $z = 36$
21. $x = 80$
22. $SH = 7$

23.

Statements	Reasons
1. $\triangle ABC$ is not isosceles. $AP \neq AC$ and $PC \neq AC$	1. Given
2. Either $\triangle APC$ is isosceles or $\triangle APC$ is not isosceles. Assume $\triangle APC$ is isosceles.	2. A statement is either true or false.
3. $AP = PC$	3. Definition of an isosceles triangle
4. $\angle 1 \cong \angle 2$	4. Given
5. $PB = PB$	5. Reflexive Property
6. $\triangle BPA \cong \triangle BPC$	6. Side-Angle-Side
7. $AB = BC$	7. C.P.C.T.C.
8. $\triangle ABC$ is isosceles.	8. Definition of an isosceles triangle
9. $\triangle APC$ is not isosceles.	9. Statement 8 contradicts the given statement that $\triangle ABC$ is not isosceles. The assumption made in statement 2 must be false. By elimination, statement 9 must be true.

24.

Statements	Reasons
1. $ABCD$ is an isosceles trapezoid with $\overline{AB} \cong \overline{CD}$.	1. Given
2. $\angle BAD \cong \angle CDA$	2. The base angles of an isosceles trapezoid are congruent.
3. $\overline{AD} \cong \overline{AD}$	3. Reflexive Property
4. $\triangle BAD \cong \triangle CDA$	4. Side-Angle-Side
5. $\overline{AC} \cong \overline{BD}$	5. C.P.C.T.C.

Practice 52
a. $\overline{RW}$ or $\overline{WR}$
b. $\overline{DE}$ or $\overline{ED}$
c. B
d. $x = 14$
e.

Statements	Reasons
1. Parallelogram $MNOP$, $MP > OP$	1. Given
2. $m\angle MOP > m\angle OMP$	2. If Unequal Sides, then Unequal Angles
3. $\overline{NM} \parallel \overline{OP}$	3. Definition of a parallelogram
4. $m\angle NMO = m\angle MOP$	4. If two parallel lines are cut by a transversal, then their alternate interior angles are equal.
5. $m\angle NMO > m\angle OMP$	5. Substitution Property of Inequality

Problem Set 52
1. True
2. False
3. B
4. D
5. 360
6. D
7. B
8. A
9. B
10. B
11. A
12. $\overline{JF}$ or $\overline{FJ}$
13. $\angle B$
14. $\overline{BC}$ or $\overline{CB}$
15. D
16. A
17. 42, 69, 69
18. E

19. $z = 130$
20. $e = 111$
21. $y = 42$
22. $x = 18$

23.

Statements	Reasons
1. $ABCD$ and $AFGH$ are parallelograms.	1. Given
2. $\angle G \cong \angle A$ and $\angle A \cong \angle C$	2. Pairs of opposite angles of a parallelogram are congruent.
3. $\angle G \cong \angle C$	3. Transitive Property

24.

Statements	Reasons
1. Parallelogram $DFGJ$, $DJ > DF$	1. Given
2. $m\angle DFJ > m\angle DJF$	2. If Unequal Sides, then Unequal Angles
3. $\overline{FD} \parallel \overline{GJ}$	3. Definition of a parallelogram
4. $m\angle GJF = m\angle DFJ$	4. If two parallel lines are cut by a transversal, then their alternate interior angles are equal.
5. $m\angle GJF > m\angle DJF$	5. Substitution Property of Inequality

Practice 53

a. $\overline{CD}$ or $\overline{DC}$
b. 6.5
c. C
d. $y = 1$
e.

Statements	Reasons
1. Parallelogram $DEFG$	1. Given
2. $\overline{DE} \cong \overline{GF}$	2. If a quadrilateral is a parallelogram, then both pairs of opposite sides are congruent.
3. $\overline{DE} \parallel \overline{GF}$	3. Definition of a parallelogram
4. $\angle EDH \cong \angle GFI$	4. If two parallel lines are cut by a transversal, then their alternate interior angles are congruent.
5. $\overline{DH} \cong \overline{FI}$	5. Given

6. $\triangle DEH \cong \triangle FGI$	6. Side-Angle-Side
7. $\angle DEH \cong \angle FGI$	7. C.P.C.T.C.

Problem Set 53

1. True
2. True
3. D
4. B
5. E
6. A
7. D
8. C
9. B
10. Converse: False
Inverse: False
Contrapositive: True
11. Converse: False
Inverse: False
Contrapositive: True
12. $\overline{BP}$ or $\overline{PB}$
13. $\overline{PT}$ or $\overline{TP}$
14. 5.5
15. D
16. E
17. $p + q = 70$
18. $x = 48$
19. $y = 10$
20. $x = 16$
21. $m\angle E = 75$, $m\angle F = 25$
22. 62, 28

23.

Statements	Reasons
1. $\overline{BM}$ is an altitude of $\triangle ABC$.	1. Given
2. $\overline{BM} \perp \overline{AC}$	2. Definition of an altitude
3. $\angle AMB$ and $\angle CMB$ are right angles.	3. Perpendicular lines intersect to form right angles.
4. $\triangle AMB$ and $\triangle CMB$ are right triangles.	4. Definition of a right triangle
5. $\overline{AB} \cong \overline{BC}$	5. Given
6. $\overline{BM} \cong \overline{BM}$	6. Reflexive Property
7. $\triangle AMB \cong \triangle CMB$	7. Hypotenuse-Leg
8. $\overline{AM} \cong \overline{MC}$	8. C.P.C.T.C.
9. Point M is the midpoint of $\overline{AC}$.	9. Definition of a midpoint

24.

Statements	Reasons
1. Parallelogram $SPQT$	1. Given

2.	$\overline{PS} \cong \overline{QT}$	2. If a quadrilateral is a parallelogram, then both pairs of opposite sides are congruent.
3.	$\overline{PS} \parallel \overline{QT}$	3. Definition of a parallelogram
4.	$\angle SPK \cong \angle QTL$	4. If two parallel lines are cut by a transversal, their alternate interior angles are congruent.
5.	$\overline{PK} \cong \overline{TL}$	5. Given
6.	$\triangle PSK \cong \triangle TQL$	6. Side-Angle-Side
7.	$\angle PSK \cong \angle TQL$	7. C.P.C.T.C.

Practice 54

a. C
b. C
c. E
d. $m\angle EKD = 85$
e. Statements

	Statements	Reasons
1.	Isosceles trapezoid $MNPQ$, $\angle QSP \cong \angle QPS$	1. Given
2.	$\angle MNS \cong \angle QPS$	2. The upper base angles of an isosceles trapezoid are congruent.
3.	$\angle MNS \cong \angle QSP$	3. Transitive Property
4.	$\overline{MN} \parallel \overline{SQ}$	4. If two lines form congruent corresponding angles with a transversal, then the lines are parallel.
5.	$\overline{MQ} \parallel \overline{NS}$	5. Definition of an isosceles trapezoid
6.	$MNSQ$ is a parallelogram.	6. Definition of a parallelogram

Problem Set 54

1. True
2. True
3. C
4. D
5. 360
6. A
7. C
8. B
9. C
10. B

11. A
12. C
13. A
14. $\overline{HJ}$ or $\overline{JH}$
15. $\angle A$
16. D
17. E
18. B
19. $a + b = 180$
20. $y = 144$
21. $x = 5$
22. $m\angle TQR = 80$

23. Statements

	Statements	Reasons
1.	Isosceles trapezoid $PQST$	1. Given
2.	$\overline{QP} \cong \overline{ST}$	2. Definition of an isosceles trapezoid
3.	$\angle PQS \cong \angle TSQ$	3. The upper base angles of an isosceles trapezoid are congruent.
4.	$\overline{QS} \cong \overline{QS}$	4. Reflexive Property
5.	$\triangle PQS \cong \triangle TSQ$	5. Side-Angle-Side
6.	$\angle QSU \cong \angle TQS$	6. C.P.C.T.C.
7.	$\overline{QU} \cong \overline{US}$	7. Converse of the Base Angles Theorem
8.	$\triangle QSU$ is isosceles.	8. Definition of an isosceles triangle

24. Statements

	Statements	Reasons
1.	Isosceles trapezoid $EFGH$, $\angle FEJ \cong \angle FJE$	1. Given
2.	$\angle FEJ \cong \angle GHJ$	2. The lower base angles of an isosceles trapezoid are congruent.
3.	$\angle FJE \cong \angle GHJ$	3. Transitive Property
4.	$\overline{FJ} \parallel \overline{GH}$	4. If two lines form congruent corresponding angles with a transversal, then the lines are parallel.
5.	$\overline{FG} \parallel \overline{JH}$	5. Definition of an isosceles trapezoid
6.	$FGHJ$ is a parallelogram.	6. Definition of a parallelogram

Practice 55

a. D

b. $p = 65$, $q = 115$, $r = 115$, $s = 65$

c. $x = 5$, $y = 7$

d. 155, 25

e.

Statements	Reasons
1. $\triangle KJL \cong \triangle NML$	1. Given
2. $\overline{KJ} \cong \overline{MN}$	2. C.P.C.T.C.
3. N is the midpoint of $\overline{MO}$.	3. Given
4. $\overline{MN} \cong \overline{NO}$	4. Definition of a midpoint
5. $\overline{KJ} \cong \overline{NO}$	5. Transitive Property
6. $\angle M \cong \angle KJL$	6. C.P.C.T.C.
7. $\overline{KJ} \parallel \overline{NO}$	7. If two lines form congruent alternate interior angles with a transversal, then the lines are parallel.
8. $KJON$ is a parallelogram.	8. If one pair of opposite sides is both parallel and congruent, then a quadrilateral is a parallelogram.

Problem Set 55

1. False
2. False
3. E
4. B
5. A
6. D
7. Converse: True
   Inverse: True
   Contrapositive: False
8. Converse: True
   Inverse: True
   Contrapositive: False
9. $\angle C$
10. $\angle K$
11. $\overline{WR}$ or $\overline{RW}$
12. A
13. C
14. E
15. D
16. A
17. $x = 51$
18. $u = 70$, $x = 110$, $y = 110$, $z = 70$
19. $x = 82$, $y = 98$, $z = 98$
20. $x = 4$, $y = 6$
21. 34, 56
22. 125, 55

23.

Statements	Reasons
1. $\triangle BCD \cong \triangle EFD$	1. Given
2. $\overline{BC} \cong \overline{EF}$	2. C.P.C.T.C.
3. B is the midpoint of $\overline{AC}$.	3. Given
4. $\overline{AB} \cong \overline{BC}$	4. Definition of a midpoint
5. $\overline{AB} \cong \overline{EF}$	5. Transitive Property
6. $\angle C \cong \angle DFE$	6. C.P.C.T.C.
7. $\overline{AB} \parallel \overline{EF}$	7. If two lines form congruent alternate interior angles with a transversal, then the lines are parallel.
8. $ABEF$ is a parallelogram.	8. If one pair of opposite sides is both parallel and congruent, then a quadrilateral is a parallelogram.

24. (5) $AE = EC$ (Definition of a midpoint)
    (6) $\angle 1 \cong \angle 2$ (Pairs of vertical angles are congruent.)
    (7) $\triangle ADE \cong \triangle CFE$ (Side-Angle-Side)
    (8) $\angle 3 \cong \angle 4$, $DA = CF$ (C.P.C.T.C.)
    (9) D is the midpoint of $\overline{AB}$. (Given)
    (10) $BD = DA$ (Definition of a midpoint)
    (11) $BD = CF$ (Transitive Property)
    (12) $\overline{BA} \parallel \overline{CF}$ (If two lines form congruent alternate interior angles with a transversal, then the lines are parallel.)
    (13) $BCFD$ is a parallelogram. (If one pair of opposite sides is both parallel and congruent, then the quadrilateral is a parallelogram.)
    (14) $\overline{DF} \parallel \overline{BC}$ and $DF = BC$ (If a quadrilateral is a parallelogram, then both pairs of opposite sides are parallel and congruent.)
    (15) $DE = \frac{1}{2}DF$ (Definition of a midpoint)
    (16) $DE = \frac{1}{2}BC$ (Substitution Property)

Practice 56

a. E
b. E
c. B
d. $y = 4$

e.

Statements	Reasons
1. $ABCD$ is a rhombus.	1. Given
2. $\overline{AB} \cong \overline{BC} \cong \overline{CD} \cong \overline{AD}$	2. Definition of a rhombus
3. $\overline{BE} \cong \overline{CF}$, $\overline{CE} \cong \overline{FD}$	3. Given
4. $\triangle CBE \cong \triangle DCF$	4. Side-Side-Side
5. $\angle B \cong \angle DCF$	5. C.P.C.T.C.
6. $\overline{AB} \parallel \overline{CD}$	6. Definition of a rhombus/parallelogram
7. $m\angle B + m\angle DCF = 180$	7. If two parallel lines are cut by a transversal, interior angles on the same side of the transversal are supplementary.
8. $m\angle B + m\angle B = 180$ or $2m\angle B = 180$	8. Substitution Property
9. $m\angle B = 90$	9. Division Property
10. $m\angle DCF = 90$	10. Substitution Property
11. $m\angle A = 90$, $m\angle ADC = 90$	11. Pairs of opposite angles in a rhombus/parallelogram are equal.
12. $ABCD$ is a square.	12. Definition of a square

Problem Set 56

1. True
2. True
3. C
4. D
5. A
6. B
7. A
8. E
9. E
10. A
11. C
12. B
13. A
14. B
15. 20, 40, 120
16. 30, 60, 90
17. $\angle D$
18. $\overline{AB}$ or $\overline{BA}$
19. $b = 5$
20. C
21. $g = 30$
22. $x = 3$

23.

Statements	Reasons
1. Rectangle $DEFG$	1. Given
2. $\angle E$ and $\angle F$ are right angles.	2. Definition of a rectangle
3. $\angle E \cong \angle F$	3. All right angles are congruent.
4. T is the midpoint of $\overline{EF}$.	4. Given
5. $\overline{ET} \cong \overline{TF}$	5. Definition of a midpoint
6. $\overline{ED} \cong \overline{FG}$	6. If a quadrilateral is a rectangle/parallelogram, then both pairs of opposite sides are congruent.
7. $\triangle DET \cong \triangle GFT$	7. Side-Angle-Side
8. $\overline{DT} \cong \overline{GT}$	8. C.P.C.T.C.
9. $\triangle DTG$ is isosceles.	9. Definition of an isosceles triangle

24.

Statements	Reasons
1. $JKLM$ is a rhombus.	1. Given
2. $\overline{JK} \cong \overline{KL} \cong \overline{LM} \cong \overline{JM}$	2. Definition of a rhombus
3. $\overline{KP} \cong \overline{JQ}$, $\overline{LP} \cong \overline{KQ}$	3. Given
4. $\triangle KJQ \cong \triangle LKP$	4. Side-Side-Side
5. $\angle LKP \cong \angle J$	5. C.P.C.T.C.
6. $\overline{KL} \parallel \overline{JM}$	6. Definition of a rhombus/parallelogram
7. $m\angle LKP + m\angle J = 180$	7. If two parallel lines are cut by a transversal, then interior angles on the same side of the transversal are supplementary.
8. $m\angle J + m\angle J = 180$ or $2m\angle J = 180$	8. Substitution Property
9. $m\angle J = 90$	9. Division Property
10. $m\angle LKP = 90$	10. Substitution Property

11.	$m\angle M = 90$, $m\angle KLM = 90$	11. Pairs of opposite angles in a rhombus/parallelogram are equal.
12.	$JKLM$ is a square.	12. Definition of a square

Practice 57

a. Converse: False
Inverse: False
Contrapositive: True

b. D

c. $a = 9$, $b = 126$, $c = 126$

d. $m\angle ADC = 95$

e.

	Statements		Reasons
1.	Rhombus $LJNK$	1.	Given
2.	$\overline{KN} \cong \overline{KL}$, $\overline{NJ} \cong \overline{LJ}$	2.	Definition of a rhombus
3.	$\angle L \cong \angle N$	3.	Both pairs of opposite angles of a rhombus/ parallelogram are congruent.
4.	$\triangle JNK \cong \triangle JLK$	4.	Side-Angle-Side
5.	$\angle 1 \cong \angle 2$, $\angle 3 \cong \angle 4$	5.	C.P.C.T.C.

Problem Set 57

1. False
2. True
3. B
4. C
5. E
6. B
7. A
8. D
9. A
10. Converse: False
Inverse: False
Contrapositive: True
11. Converse: False
Inverse: False
Contrapositive: True
12. 8.5
13. $\angle A$
14. E
15. C
16. D
17. $x = 50$
18. $m\angle S = 68$, $m\angle D = 112$
19. $x = 15$, $y = 105$, $z = 105$
20. $m\angle DPI = 116$
21. $m\angle A = 80$, $m\angle B = 40$

22. 50, 40

23.

	Statements		Reasons
1.	Rectangle $ATPZ$	1.	Given
2.	$\overline{AT} \cong \overline{ZP}$	2.	Both pairs of opposite sides of a rectangle/parallelogram are congruent.
3.	$\angle T \cong \angle Z$	3.	Both pairs of opposite angles of a rectangle/ parallelogram are congruent.
4.	$\overline{TV} \cong \overline{BZ}$	4.	Given
5.	$\triangle TAV \cong \triangle ZPB$	5.	Side-Angle-Side
6.	$\overline{AV} \cong \overline{PB}$	6.	C.P.C.T.C.

24.

	Statements		Reasons
1.	Rhombus $BCDA$	1.	Given
2.	$\overline{AD} \cong \overline{AB}$, $\overline{DC} \cong \overline{BC}$	2.	Definition of a rhombus
3.	$\angle D \cong \angle B$	3.	Both pairs of opposite angles of a rhombus/ parallelogram are congruent.
4.	$\triangle CDA \cong \triangle CBA$	4.	Side-Angle-Side
5.	$\angle 1 \cong \angle 2$, $\angle 3 \cong \angle 4$	5.	C.P.C.T.C.

CHAPTER 9

Practice 58
a. B
b. C
c. $x = 4$, $y = 3$
d. $a + b + c = 360$
e.

Statements	Reasons
1. Parallelogram *AECF*	1. Given
2. $\overline{AE} \parallel \overline{FC}$	2. Definition of a parallelogram
3. $\angle AEF \cong \angle CFE$	3. If two parallel lines are cut by a transversal, then their alternate interior angles are congruent.
4. $\angle AEF$ and $\angle AEB$ are supplementary; $\angle CFE$ and $\angle CFD$ are supplementary.	4. If two angles are a linear pair, then they are supplementary.
5. $\angle AEB \cong \angle CFD$	5. If two angles are supplementary to congruent angles, then they are congruent.
6. $\overline{BE} \cong \overline{DF}$	6. Given
7. $\overline{AE} \cong \overline{FC}$	7. If a quadrilateral is a parallelogram, then both pairs of opposite sides are congruent.
8. $\triangle AEB \cong \triangle CFD$	8. Side-Angle-Side
9. $\overline{AB} \cong \overline{CD}$	9. C.P.C.T.C.
10. $\angle ABE \cong \angle CDF$	10. C.P.C.T.C.
11. $\overline{AB} \parallel \overline{CD}$	11. If two lines form congruent alternate interior angles with a transversal, then the lines are parallel.
12. *ABCD* is a parallelogram.	12. If one pair of opposite sides is both parallel and congruent, then a quadrilateral is a parallelogram.

Problem Set 58
1. False
2. True
3. D
4. A
5. E
6. C

7. A
8. D
9. B
10. D
11. B
12. A
13. C
14. B
15. $\angle K$
16. $\overline{LW}$ or $\overline{WL}$
17. E
18. D
19. $x = 12$
20. $x = 5$, $y = 6$
21. $p = 23$, $q = 18$
22. $r + s + t = 360$
23.

Statements	Reasons
1. Rhombus *TCBV*, $\overline{CU} \perp \overline{BV}$, $\overline{CS} \perp \overline{TV}$	1. Given
2. $\angle CST$ and $\angle CUB$ are right angles.	2. Perpendicular lines intersect to form right angles.
3. $\angle CST \cong \angle CUB$	3. All right angles are congruent.
4. $\overline{CB} \cong \overline{CT}$	4. Definition of a rhombus
5. $\angle T \cong \angle B$	5. If a quadrilateral is a rhombus/parallelogram, then both pairs of opposite angles are congruent.
6. $\triangle CTS \cong \triangle CBU$	6. Angle-Angle-Side
7. $\overline{CU} \cong \overline{CS}$	7. C.P.C.T.C.

24.

Statements	Reasons
1. Parallelogram *RJTI*	1. Given
2. $\overline{RI} \parallel \overline{JT}$	2. Definition of a parallelogram
3. $\angle RIJ \cong \angle TJI$	3. If two parallel lines are cut by a transversal, then their alternate interior angles are congruent.
4. $\angle RIJ$ and $\angle RIE$ are supplementary; $\angle TJI$ and $\angle TJS$ are supplementary.	4. If two angles are a linear pair, then they are supplementary.
5. $\angle RIE \cong \angle TJS$	5. If two angles are supplementary to congruent angles, then they are congruent.

6.	$\overline{EI} \cong \overline{SJ}$	6. Given
7.	$\overline{RI} \cong \overline{JT}$	7. If a quadrilateral is a parallelogram, then both pairs of opposite sides are congruent.
8.	$\triangle RIE \cong \triangle TJS$	8. Side-Angle-Side
9.	$\overline{RE} \cong \overline{ST}$	9. C.P.C.T.C.
10.	$\angle REI \cong \angle TSJ$	10. C.P.C.T.C.
11.	$\overline{RE} \parallel \overline{ST}$	11. If two lines form congruent alternate interior angles with a transversal, then the lines are parallel.
12.	$ERST$ is a parallelogram.	12. If one pair of opposite sides is both parallel and congruent, then a quadrilateral is a parallelogram.

Practice 59
a. 540
b. E
c. $y = 88$
d. 100, 80
e.

	Statements	Reasons
1.	Quadrilateral $FGHI$, $\overline{GF} \parallel \overline{HK}$, and $\overline{GF} \cong \overline{HK}$	1. Given
2.	$GHKF$ is a parallelogram.	2. If one pair of opposite sides is both parallel and congruent, then the quadrilateral is a parallelogram.
3.	$\overline{GH} \parallel \overline{FK}$ and $\overline{GH} \parallel \overline{FI}$	3. Definition of a parallelogram
4.	$FGHI$ is a trapezoid.	4. Definition of a trapezoid

Problem Set 59
1. True
2. False
3. D
4. A
5. E
6. E
7. C
8. C
9. 720
10. 900

11. 360
12. Converse: False
Inverse: False
Contrapositive: True
13. Converse: False
Inverse: False
Contrapositive: True
14. 94, 43, 43
15. 45, 63, 72
16. D
17. C
18. $m\overline{TU} = 5$
19. $x + y + z = 270$
20. $x = 130$
21. 75, 15
22. 105, 75
23.

	Statements	Reasons
1.	$\angle B \cong \angle D$ and $\angle A \cong \angle C$	1. Given
2.	$ABCD$ is a parallelogram.	2. If both pairs of opposite angles are congruent, then a quadrilateral is a parallelogram.
3.	$\overline{AB} \cong \overline{DC}$	3. If a quadrilateral is a parallelogram, then both pairs of opposite sides are congruent.

24.

	Statements	Reasons
1.	Quadrilateral $LPRS$, $\overline{PT} \parallel \overline{RS}$, and $\overline{PT} \cong \overline{RS}$	1. Given
2.	$PRST$ is a parallelogram.	2. If one pair of opposite sides is both parallel and congruent, then the quadrilateral is a parallelogram.
3.	$\overline{PR} \parallel \overline{TS}$ and $\overline{PR} \parallel \overline{LS}$	3. Definition of a parallelogram
4.	$LPRS$ is a trapezoid.	4. Definition of a trapezoid

Practice 60
a. 360
b. C
c. D
d. $MP = 9$
e.

Statements	Reasons
1. Rectangle $ABCD$, $\overline{BP} \cong \overline{CP}$	1. Given

	Statements		Reasons
2.	$\angle PBC \cong \angle PCB$	2.	Base Angles Theorem
3.	$\overline{BC} \parallel \overline{AD}$	3.	Definition of a rectangle/ parallelogram
4.	$\angle BLA \cong \angle PBC$, $\angle CMD \cong \angle PCB$	4.	If two parallel lines are cut by a transversal, then their alternate interior angles are congruent.
5.	$\angle CMD \cong \angle PBC$	5.	Transitive Property
6.	$\angle BLA \cong \angle CMD$	6.	Transitive Property
7.	$\angle A$ and $\angle D$ are right angles.	7.	Definition of a rectangle
8.	$\angle A \cong \angle D$	8.	All right angles are congruent.
9.	$\overline{AB} \cong \overline{CD}$	9.	If a quadrilateral is a rectangle/parallelogram, then both pairs of opposite sides are congruent.
10.	$\triangle BLA \cong \triangle CMD$	10.	Angle-Angle-Side
11.	$\overline{AL} \cong \overline{DM}$	11.	C.P.C.T.C.

Problem Set 60
1. False
2. True
3. A
4. D
5. E
6. B
7. E
8. 1,080
9. 540
10. 360
11. 360
12. C
13. C
14. A
15. B
16. 20.5
17. $\angle F$
18. D
19. D
20. $r + s = 120$
21. E
22. $EA = 7$

23.
	Statements		Reasons
1.	$HIJK$ is a rectangle.	1.	Given
2.	$\overline{IK} \cong \overline{HJ}$	2.	The diagonals of a rectangle are congruent.
3.	$HIKL$ is a parallelogram.	3.	Given
4.	$\overline{IK} \cong \overline{HL}$	4.	If a quadrilateral is a parallelogram, then both pairs of opposite sides are congruent.
5.	$\overline{HJ} \cong \overline{HL}$	5.	Transitive Property
6.	$\triangle HJL$ is isosceles.	6.	Definition of an isosceles triangle

24.
	Statements		Reasons
1.	Rectangle $QPRS$, $\overline{QU} \cong \overline{SU}$	1.	Given
2.	$\angle UQS \cong \angle USQ$	2.	Base Angles Theorem
3.	$\overline{PR} \parallel \overline{QS}$	3.	Definition of a rectangle/ parallelogram
4.	$\angle PVQ \cong \angle UQS$, $\angle RTS \cong \angle USQ$	4.	If two parallel lines are cut by a transversal, then their alternate interior angles are congruent.
5.	$\angle RTS \cong \angle UQS$	5.	Transitive Property
6.	$\angle PVQ \cong \angle RTS$	6.	Transitive Property
7.	$\angle P$ and $\angle R$ are right angles.	7.	Definition of a rectangle
8.	$\angle P \cong \angle R$	8.	All right angles are congruent.
9.	$\overline{PQ} \cong \overline{RS}$	9.	If a quadrilateral is a rectangle/parallelogram, then both pairs of opposite sides are congruent.
10.	$\triangle PVQ \cong \triangle RTS$	10.	Angle-Angle-Side
11.	$\overline{PV} \cong \overline{RT}$	11.	C.P.C.T.C.

Practice 61
a. E
b. C
c. $e = 50$
d. 54, 36

e.
	Statements		Reasons
1.	$JKLM$ is a parallelogram.	1.	Given
2.	$\overline{KJ} \cong \overline{LM}$	2.	If a quadrilateral is a parallelogram, pairs of opposite sides are congruent.
3.	$\angle K \cong \angle M$	3.	If a quadrilateral is a parallelogram, pairs of opposite angles are congruent.

4.	$\overline{JP} \perp \overline{KL}$, $\overline{LN} \perp \overline{JM}$	4.	Given
5.	∠JPK and ∠LNM are right angles.	5.	Perpendicular lines intersect to form right angles.
6.	∠JPK ≅ ∠LNM	6.	All right angles are congruent.
7.	△KJP ≅ △MLN	7.	Angle-Angle-Side

Problem Set 61

1. True
2. False
3. D
4. B
5. E
6. A
7. D
8. E
9. sum of interior: 180; sum of exterior: 360
10. sum of interior: 720; sum of exterior: 360
11. D
12. A
13. Converse: True
    Inverse: True
    Contrapositive: True
14. Converse: True
    Inverse: True
    Contrapositive: True
15. B
16. E
17. B
18. $y = 140$
19. $a + b + c + d = 220$
20. $r = 36$
21. C
22. 50, 40

23.

Statements		Reasons
1.	$\overline{LQ} \cong \overline{PQ}$	1. Given
2.	∠LPQ ≅ ∠L	2. Base Angles Theorem
3.	∠L ≅ ∠HQP	3. Given
4.	∠LPQ ≅ ∠HQP	4. Transitive Property
5.	$\overline{LP} \parallel \overline{QH}$	5. If two lines form congruent alternate interior angles with a transversal, then the lines are parallel.
6.	PLQH is a trapezoid.	6. Definition of a trapezoid

24.

Statements	Reasons
1. ABCD is a parallelogram.	1. Given

2.	$\overline{AB} \cong \overline{CD}$	2.	If a quadrilateral is a parallelogram, pairs of opposite sides are congruent.
3.	∠A ≅ ∠C	3.	If a quadrilateral is a parallelogram, pairs of opposite angles are congruent.
4.	$\overline{BE} \perp \overline{AD}$, $\overline{FD} \perp \overline{BC}$	4.	Given
5.	∠BEA and ∠DFC are right angles.	5.	Perpendicular lines intersect to form right angles.
6.	∠BEA ≅ ∠DFC	6.	All right angles are congruent.
7.	△ABE ≅ △CDF	7.	Angle-Angle-Side

Practice 62

a. perimeter = 36
b. perimeter = 72
c. $a + b = 172$
d. 8

e.

Statements		Reasons
1. Quadrilateral STUR; $\overline{SU}$ and $\overline{TL}$ bisect each other.		1. Given
2. STUL is a parallelogram.		2. If the diagonals bisect each other, then a quadrilateral is a parallelogram.
3.	$\overline{ST} \parallel \overline{UL}$ and $\overline{ST} \parallel \overline{UR}$	3. Definition of a parallelogram
4.	STUR is a trapezoid.	4. Definition of a trapezoid
5.	$\overline{SR} \cong \overline{TU}$	5. Given
6.	STUR is an isosceles trapezoid.	6. Definition of an isosceles trapezoid
7.	∠R ≅ ∠RUT	7. The lower base angles of an isosceles trapezoid are congruent.

Problem Set 62

1. True
2. True
3. C
4. C
5. A
6. E
7. D

8. 900
9. 720
10. perimeter = 30
11. perimeter = 26
12. perimeter = 104
13. B
14. 60, 60, 60
15. B
16. A
17. $\overline{CD}$ or $\overline{DC}$
18. $\overline{AC}$ or $\overline{CA}$
19. D
20. A
21. $x + y = 164$
22. 10
23.

Statements	Reasons
1. $\angle RTS \cong \angle TRV$	1. Given
2. $\overline{RV} \parallel \overline{ST}$	2. If two lines form congruent alternate interior angles with a transversal, then the lines are parallel.
3. $\overline{RV} \cong \overline{ST}$	3. Given
4. $RSTV$ is a parallelogram.	4. If one pair of opposite sides is both parallel and congruent, then a quadrilateral is a parallelogram.

24.

Statements	Reasons
1. Quadrilateral $DJKL$; $\overline{JL}$ and $\overline{FK}$ bisect each other.	1. Given
2. $FJKL$ is a parallelogram.	2. If the diagonals bisect each other, then a quadrilateral is a parallelogram.
3. $\overline{JF} \parallel \overline{KL}$ and $\overline{JD} \parallel \overline{KL}$	3. Definition of a parallelogram
4. $DJKL$ is a trapezoid.	4. Definition of a trapezoid
5. $\overline{JK} \cong \overline{DL}$	5. Given
6. $DJKL$ is an isosceles trapezoid.	6. Definition of an isosceles trapezoid
7. $\angle D \cong \angle DJK$	7. The lower base angles of an isosceles trapezoid are congruent.

CHAPTER 10

Practice 63
a. Yes
b. 120, 30, 30
c. $x = 10$, $y = 10$
d. $m\angle E = 105$, $m\angle F = 35$
e. Statements

Statements	Reasons
1. Regular hexagon $OPQRST$ with diagonals $\overline{PR}$ and $\overline{TR}$	1. Given
2. $\overline{TS} \cong \overline{PQ}$, $\overline{SR} \cong \overline{QR}$	2. A regular polygon is equilateral.
3. $\angle S \cong \angle Q$	3. A regular polygon is equiangular.
4. $\triangle TSR \cong \triangle PQR$	4. Side-Angle-Side
5. $\overline{PR} \cong \overline{TR}$	5. C.P.C.T.C.

Problem Set 63
1. True
2. True
3. D
4. C
5. B
6. E
7. D
8. perimeter = 210
9. perimeter = $27\frac{2}{3}$
10. Yes
11. Yes
12. No
13. 90, 70, 20
14. 36, 72, 72
15. C
16. A
17. A
18. B
19. $x = 8$, $y = 12$
20. $w + u = 90$
21. 45, 135
22. $m\angle D = 104$, $m\angle R = 26$
23. Statements

Statements	Reasons
1. Trapezoid $ABCE$ with bases $\overline{AE}$ and $\overline{BC}$	1. Given
2. $\overline{AE} \parallel \overline{BC}$	2. Definition of a trapezoid
3. $\overline{AD} \cong \overline{BC}$	3. Given

Statements	Reasons
4. $ABCD$ is a parallelogram.	4. If one pair of opposite sides is both parallel and congruent, then a quadrilateral is a parallelogram.

24.

Statements	Reasons
1. Regular octagon $ABCDEFGH$ with diagonals $\overline{HF}$ and $\overline{DF}$	1. Given
2. $\overline{HG} \cong \overline{DE}$, $\overline{GF} \cong \overline{EF}$	2. A regular polygon is equilateral.
3. $\angle G \cong \angle E$	3. A regular polygon is equiangular.
4. $\triangle HGF \cong \triangle DEF$	4. Side-Angle-Side
5. $\overline{HF} \cong \overline{DF}$	5. C.P.C.T.C.

Practice 64
a. perimeter = 52
b. 18
c. $y = 19$
d. 208 lip synchers
e. Statements

Statements	Reasons
1. F is the midpoint of $\overline{EJ}$ and G is the midpoint of $\overline{DJ}$.	1. Given
2. $\overline{ED} \parallel \overline{FG}$	2. The line segment joining the midpoints of two sides of a triangle is parallel to the third side and is one-half of its length.
3. $m\angle FGJ = m\angle D$	3. If two parallel lines are cut by a transversal, then their corresponding angles are congruent.
4. $m\angle FGJ > m\angle J$	4. Given
5. $m\angle D > m\angle J$	5. Substitution Property of Inequality
6. $EJ > DE$	6. If Unequal Angles, then Unequal Sides

Problem Set 64
1. False
2. False
3. C
4. A
5. C

6. 540
7. 1,260
8. perimeter = 21
9. perimeter = 42
10. means: 4, 24; extremes: 3, 32
11. means: t, u; extremes: s, v
12. 8
13. 10
14. $x = 7$
15. $y = 11$
16. $\angle B$
17. $\angle X$
18. $x = 70$
19. $x = 60$, $y = 20$, $z = 30$
20. $d = 24$
21. 12
22. 46,875 men subscribers

23.
Statements	Reasons
1. $\overline{AB} \cong \overline{DC}$, $\overline{AD} \cong \overline{BC}$	1. Given
2. $ABCD$ is a parallelogram.	2. If both pairs of opposite sides are congruent, then a quadrilateral is a parallelogram.
3. $\angle A$ and $\angle B$ are supplementary.	3. If a quadrilateral is a parallelogram, then consecutive angles are supplementary.

24.
Statements	Reasons
1. P is the midpoint of $\overline{CL}$ and V is the midpoint of $\overline{CT}$.	1. Given
2. $\overline{LT} \parallel \overline{PV}$	2. The line segment joining the midpoints of two sides of a triangle is parallel to the third side and is one-half of its length.
3. $m\angle PVC = m\angle T$	3. If two parallel lines are cut by a transversal, then their corresponding angles are congruent.
4. $m\angle PVC > m\angle C$	4. Given
5. $m\angle T > m\angle C$	5. Substitution Property of Inequality
6. $CL > LT$	6. If Unequal Angles, then Unequal Sides

Practice 65

a. C
b. E
c. Similar
d. 3,000 dogs
e.
Statements	Reasons
1. Rhombus $ABCD$ with diagonals $\overline{AC}$ and $\overline{BD}$	1. Given
2. $\overline{AC} \perp \overline{BD}$	2. The diagonals of a rhombus are perpendicular to each other.
3. $\angle BOC$ is a right angle.	3. Perpendicular lines intersect to form right angles.
4. $\triangle BOC$ is a right triangle.	4. Definition of a right triangle
5. $\angle OBC$ and $\angle OCB$ are complementary.	5. The acute angles of a right triangle are complementary.

Problem Set 65

1. True
2. False
3. True
4. D
5. B
6. A
7. C
8. perimeter = 29
9. B
10. Not proportional
11. Not proportional
12. 14
13. $\sqrt{66}$
14. $x = 48$
15. E
16. Similar
17. Not similar
18. Similar
19. $s + u = 250$
20. $x = 21$
21. perimeter = 224
22. 2,000 calls

23.
Statements	Reasons
1. $\overline{GI}$ and $\overline{FH}$ are altitudes to $\overline{DH}$ and $\overline{DG}$; $\angle HGF \cong \angle IHG$	1. Given
2. $\overline{DG} \cong \overline{DH}$	2. Converse of the Base Angles Theorem
3. $\triangle DGH$ is isosceles.	3. Definition of an isosceles triangle

| 4. | $\overline{GI} \cong \overline{FH}$ | 4. The altitudes extending to the legs of an isosceles triangle are congruent. |

24.

	Statements		Reasons
1.	Rhombus $RTUV$ with diagonals $\overline{RU}$ and $\overline{TV}$	1.	Given
2.	$\overline{RU} \perp \overline{TV}$	2.	The diagonals of a rhombus are perpendicular to each other.
3.	$\angle TQU$ is a right angle.	3.	Perpendicular lines intersect to form right angles.
4.	$\triangle TQU$ is a right triangle.	4.	Definition of a right triangle
5.	$\angle QTU$ and $\angle QUT$ are complementary.	5.	The acute angles of a right triangle are complementary.

Practice 66

a. Similar
b. 12.78 (or $12.78:1$)
c. $a = 112.5$
d. 20 grams
e.

	Statements		Reasons
1.	Rhombus $FGHI$	1.	Given
2.	$\overline{GI}$ and $\overline{FH}$ are perpendicular.	2.	The diagonals of a rhombus are perpendicular.
3.	$\angle HPG$ and $\angle FPG$ are right angles.	3.	Perpendicular lines intersect to form right angles.
4.	$\angle HPG \cong \angle FPG$	4.	All right angles are congruent.
5.	$\overline{FP} \cong \overline{PH}$	5.	If a quadrilateral is a rhombus/parallelogram, then the diagonals bisect each other.
6.	$\overline{JP} \cong \overline{JP}$	6.	Reflexive Property
7.	$\triangle FJP \cong \triangle HJP$	7.	Side-Angle-Side
8.	$\overline{FJ} \cong \overline{JH}$	8.	C.P.C.T.C.
9.	$\triangle FJH$ is isosceles.	9.	Definition of an isosceles triangle

Problem Set 66

1. False
2. False
3. E
4. D
5. E
6. C
7. A
8. Not similar
9. Similar
10. A
11. A
12. $1:7$
13. 28.8 (or $28.8:1$)
14. $r = 12$
15. B
16. B
17. D
18. $x = 68$
19. $y = 100$
20. $z = 90$
21. 25 feet
22. 8 grams

23.

	Statements		Reasons
1.	$RS = TU$, $\angle VTR \cong \angle WSU$, $\angle VRT \cong \angle WUS$	1.	Given
2.	$ST = ST$	2.	Reflexive Property
3.	$RS + ST = ST + TU$	3.	Addition Property
4.	$RT = RS + ST$ and $SU = ST + TU$	4.	Betweenness of Points
5.	$RT = SU$	5.	Substitution Property
6.	$\triangle RVT \cong \triangle UWS$	6.	Angle-Side-Angle

24.

	Statements		Reasons
1.	Rhombus $ABCD$	1.	Given
2.	$\overline{DB} \perp \overline{AC}$	2.	The diagonals of a rhombus are perpendicular.
3.	$\angle DOC$ and $\angle COB$ are right angles.	3.	Perpendicular lines intersect to form right angles.
4.	$\angle DOC \cong \angle COB$	4.	All right angles are congruent.
5.	$\overline{DO} \cong \overline{OB}$	5.	If a quadrilateral is a rhombus/parallelogram, then the diagonals bisect each other.
6.	$\overline{OP} \cong \overline{OP}$	6.	Reflexive Property
7.	$\triangle DOP \cong \triangle BOP$	7.	Side-Angle-Side

8.	$\overline{DP} \cong \overline{PB}$	8. C.P.C.T.C.
9.	$\triangle DPB$ is isosceles.	9. Definition of an isosceles triangle

Practice 67

a. $? = KQ$ or QK

b. $\dfrac{HJ}{HP} = \dfrac{5}{2}$; $\dfrac{IJ}{IK} = \dfrac{5}{2}$; Sides are divided proportionally.

c. A

d. $x = 42$

e. Statements

Statements	Reasons
1. $\triangle MCA$ and rectangle $BCDN$	1. Given
2. $\overline{BC} \parallel \overline{ND}$ and $\overline{BN} \parallel \overline{CD}$	2. Definition of a rectangle/parallelogram
3. $\dfrac{DM}{DC} = \dfrac{MN}{NA}$ and $\dfrac{MN}{NA} = \dfrac{BC}{AB}$	3. If a line is parallel to one side of a triangle and intersects the other two sides, then the line divides those sides proportionally.
4. $\dfrac{DM}{DC} = \dfrac{BC}{AB}$	4. Transitive Property

Problem Set 67

1. True

2. True

3. C

4. E

5. B

6. C

7. D

8. $? = LT$ or TL

9. $? = LP$ or PL

10. $\dfrac{EC}{BE} = \dfrac{3}{4}$; $\dfrac{OA}{BO} = \dfrac{3}{4}$; Sides are divided proportionally.

11. $\dfrac{BA}{OA} = \dfrac{7}{3}$; $\dfrac{BC}{EC} = \dfrac{7}{3}$; Sides are divided proportionally.

12. C

13. perimeter $= 28$

14. $x = 36$

15. $y = \dfrac{m}{3}$

16. $\angle C$

17. $\angle X$

18. $x = 65$

19. $y = 40$

20. $x = 80$

21. $m\angle G = 54$

22. 30, 150

23. Statements

Statements	Reasons
1. B is the midpoint of $\overline{AC}$ and D is the midpoint of $\overline{CE}$.	1. Given
2. $AB = \dfrac{1}{2} AC$ and $ED = \dfrac{1}{2} CE$	2. Definition of a midpoint
3. $m\angle E > m\angle A$	3. Given
4. $AC > CE$	4. If Unequal Angles, then Unequal Sides
5. $\dfrac{1}{2} AC > \dfrac{1}{2} CE$	5. Multiplication Property of Inequality
6. $AB > ED$	6. Substitution Property of Inequality

24. Statements

Statements	Reasons
1. $\triangle DHF$ and rectangle $EJHP$	1. Given
2. $\overline{EJ} \parallel \overline{PH}$ and $\overline{EP} \parallel \overline{JH}$	2. Definition of a rectangle/parallelogram
3. $\dfrac{FJ}{JH} = \dfrac{FE}{ED}$ and $\dfrac{FE}{ED} = \dfrac{HP}{PD}$	3. If a line is parallel to one side of a triangle and intersects the other two sides, then the line divides those sides proportionally.
4. $\dfrac{FJ}{JH} = \dfrac{HP}{PD}$	4. Transitive Property

Practice 68

a. $\dfrac{BP}{PC} = \dfrac{4}{5}$; $\dfrac{AM}{MC} = \dfrac{8}{11}$; $\overline{AB}$ is not parallel to $\overline{PM}$.

b. $1:5$

c. Similar

d. 36 men

e. Statements

Statements	Reasons
1. $\triangle ABC$ with altitudes $\overline{AK}$ and $\overline{CJ}$	1. Given
2. $\overline{AK} \perp \overline{BC}$ and $\overline{CJ} \perp \overline{AB}$	2. Definition of an altitude

3.	$\angle AKC$ and $\angle CJA$ are right angles.	3.	Perpendicular lines intersect to form right angles.
4.	$\angle AKC \cong \angle CJA$	4.	All right angles are congruent.
5.	$\angle JOA \cong \angle KOC$	5.	Pairs of vertical angles are congruent.
6.	$\triangle JOA \sim \triangle KOC$	6.	Angle-Angle Similarity

Problem Set 68

1. True
2. True
3. C
4. A
5. D
6. 900
7. 360
8. $\dfrac{BW}{WC} = \dfrac{5}{6}$; $\dfrac{AT}{TC} = \dfrac{5}{6}$; Sides are divided proportionally.
9. $\dfrac{BC}{BW} = \dfrac{11}{5}$; $\dfrac{AC}{AT} = \dfrac{11}{5}$; Sides are divided proportionally.
10. $\dfrac{GI}{FG} = \dfrac{2}{3}$; $\dfrac{HE}{FH} = \dfrac{13}{19}$; $\overline{IE}$ is not parallel to $\overline{GH}$.
11. $\dfrac{FI}{IG} = \dfrac{1}{2}$; $\dfrac{FE}{EH} = \dfrac{6}{13}$; $\overline{IE}$ is not parallel to $\overline{GH}$.
12. 16
13. 21
14. $1:48$
15. $1:2$
16. Similar
17. Similar
18. Similar
19. $x = 100$
20. $y = 130$
21. 27 grams
22. 24 girls

23.

	Statements		Reasons
1.	$\overline{AC} \cong \overline{CE}$	1.	Given
2.	$\angle A \cong \angle E$	2.	Base Angles Theorem
3.	$\overline{RZ} \perp \overline{AE}$, $\overline{LV} \perp \overline{AE}$	3.	Given
4.	$\angle RZE$ and $\angle LVA$ are right angles.	4.	Perpendicular lines intersect to form right angles.
5.	$\angle RZE \cong \angle LVA$	5.	All right angles are congruent.

6.	$\triangle RZE \sim \triangle LVA$	6.	Angle-Angle Similarity

24.

	Statements		Reasons
1.	$\triangle PRD$ with altitudes $\overline{LD}$ and $\overline{PS}$	1.	Given
2.	$\overline{LD} \perp \overline{PR}$ and $\overline{PS} \perp \overline{RD}$	2.	Definition of an altitude
3.	$\angle PLD$ and $\angle PSD$ are right angles.	3.	Perpendicular lines intersect to form right angles.
4.	$\angle PLD \cong \angle PSD$	4.	All right angles are congruent.
5.	$\angle LEP \cong \angle SED$	5.	Pairs of vertical angles are congruent.
6.	$\triangle LEP \sim \triangle SED$	6.	Angle-Angle Similarity

Practice 69

a. $? = 15$; $x = 14$
b. E
c. $x = 130$
d. 48, 132, 48, 132

e.

	Statements		Reasons
1.	$\triangle ABC \sim \triangle PLM$	1.	Given
2.	$\angle ABC \cong \angle PLM$, $\angle ACB \cong \angle PML$	2.	Converse of the definition of similar triangles
3.	$\triangle ABC \sim \triangle XYZ$	3.	Given
4.	$\angle ABC \cong \angle XYZ$, $\angle ACB \cong \angle XZY$	4.	Converse of the definition of similar triangles
5.	$\angle PLM \cong \angle XYZ$, $\angle PML \cong \angle XZY$	5.	Transitive Property
6.	$\triangle PLM \sim \triangle XYZ$	6.	Angle-Angle Similarity

Problem Set 69

1. True
2. True
3. D
4. D
5. B
6. B
7. C
8. $? = 9$; $x = 12$
9. $? = 24$; $x = 12$
10. $p = 14$
11. $k = \dfrac{17}{3}$

12. perimeter = 29 inches
13. perimeter = 63 centimeters
14. E
15. A
16. C
17. A
18. E
19. $x = 75$
20. $y = 120$
21. perimeter = 112 inches
22. 60, 120, 60, 120
23. Statements / Reasons

	Statements		Reasons
1.	$\overline{KI} \cong \overline{IL}$, $\overline{NM} \cong \overline{ML}$	1.	Given
2.	$\dfrac{KI}{NM} = \dfrac{IL}{ML}$	2.	Division Property
3.	$\angle KIL \cong \angle NML$	3.	Given
4.	$\triangle KIL \sim \triangle NML$	4.	Side-Angle-Side Similarity

24. Statements / Reasons

	Statements		Reasons
1.	$\triangle ABC \sim \triangle PLM$	1.	Given
2.	$\angle ABC \cong \angle PLM$, $\angle ACB \cong \angle PML$	2.	Converse of the definition of similar triangles
3.	$\triangle PLM \sim \triangle XYZ$	3.	Given
4.	$\angle PLM \cong \angle XYZ$, $\angle PML \cong \angle XZY$	4.	Converse of the definition of similar triangles
5.	$\angle ABC \cong \angle XYZ$, $\angle ACB \cong \angle XZY$	5.	Transitive Property
6.	$\triangle ABC \sim \triangle XYZ$	6.	Angle-Angle Similarity

Practice 70
a. A
b. D
c. E
d. 84 inches
e. Statements / Reasons

	Statements		Reasons
1.	$\overline{KL} \parallel \overline{MN}$ and $\overline{JL} \parallel \overline{ON}$	1.	Given
2.	$\angle K \cong \angle NMO$, $\angle NOM \cong \angle J$	2.	If two parallel lines are cut by a transversal, then their corresponding angles are congruent.
3.	$\triangle JKL \sim \triangle OMN$	3.	Angle-Angle Similarity
4.	$\dfrac{KL}{MN} = \dfrac{JL}{ON}$	4.	Converse of the definition of similar triangles

5.	$KL \times ON = MN \times JL$	5.	In a proportion, the product of the means is equal to the product of the extremes.

Problem Set 70
1. True
2. True
3. D
4. B
5. C
6. 360
7. 360
8. B
9. A
10. E
11. perimeter = 36
12. $\angle P$
13. $\overline{XZ}$ or $\overline{ZX}$
14. D
15. B
16. D
17. E
18. A
19. $x = 100$
20. $y = 30$
21. 77 kennel guests
22. 70 inches
23. Statements / Reasons

	Statements		Reasons
1.	$\triangle JKL \sim \triangle STV$	1.	Given
2.	$m\angle L = m\angle V$ and $m\angle JKL = m\angle STV$	2.	Converse of the definition of similar triangles
3.	$\dfrac{1}{2}m\angle JKL = \dfrac{1}{2}m\angle STV$	3.	Multiplication Property
4.	$\overline{KP}$ bisects $\angle JKL$ and $\overline{TO}$ bisects $\angle STV$.	4.	Given
5.	$\dfrac{1}{2}m\angle JKL = m\angle PKL$ and $\dfrac{1}{2}m\angle STV = m\angle OTV$	5.	Definition of an angle bisector
6.	$m\angle PKL = m\angle OTV$	6.	Substitution Property
7.	$\triangle KPL \sim \triangle TOV$	7.	Angle-Angle Similarity

24. Statements / Reasons

	Statements		Reasons
1.	$\overline{AB} \parallel \overline{DE}$, $\overline{CB} \parallel \overline{FE}$	1.	Given

2.

$\angle A \cong \angle FDE$, $\angle DFE \cong \angle C$

2. If two parallel lines are cut by a transversal, then their corresponding angles are congruent.

3. $\triangle ABC \sim \triangle DEF$

3. Angle-Angle Similarity

4. $\dfrac{DE}{AB} = \dfrac{FE}{CB}$

4. Converse of the definition of similar triangles

5. $DE \times CB = AB \times FE$

5. In a proportion, the product of the means is equal to the product of the extremes.

Practice 71
a. A
b. B
c. perimeter = 12
d. $PO = 10$, $WC = 8$
e. Statements — Reasons

1. $\overline{GJ} \parallel \overline{DF}$ — 1. Given
2. $\angle IHF \cong \angle GIH$ — 2. If two parallel lines are cut by a transversal, then their alternate interior angles are congruent.
3. $\overline{GH} \parallel \overline{EF}$ — 3. Given
4. $\angle HEF \cong \angle IHG$ — 4. If two parallel lines are cut by a transversal, then their alternate interior angles are congruent.
5. $\triangle HEF \sim \triangle IHG$ — 5. Angle-Angle Similarity
6. $\dfrac{EF}{HG} = \dfrac{HF}{IG}$ — 6. Converse of the definition of similar triangles
7. $HG \times HF = IG \times EF$ — 7. In a proportion, the product of the means is equal to the product of the extremes.

Problem Set 71
1. True
2. False
3. False
4. C
5. E
6. D
7. A

8. B
9. A
10. E
11. $m\angle AOC = 51$
12. C
13. D
14. A
15. B
16. D
17. C
18. $x = 50$
19. $y = 45$
20. perimeter = 18
21. $BT = 18$, $DA = 6$
22. $AP = 12$, $FQ = 8$

23. Statements — Reasons

1. $\triangle DFC$, $\triangle BAC$, and $\dfrac{FC}{AC} = \dfrac{DC}{BC}$ — 1. Given
2. $\angle C \cong \angle C$ — 2. Reflexive Property
3. $\triangle DFC \sim \triangle BAC$ — 3. Side-Angle-Side Similarity
4. $\dfrac{\text{perimeter } \triangle DFC}{\text{perimeter } \triangle BAC} = \dfrac{FD}{AB}$ — 4. If two triangles are similar, then their perimeters have the same ratio as any pair of corresponding sides.

24. Statements — Reasons

1. $\overline{VZ} \parallel \overline{TR}$ — 1. Given
2. $\angle WUT \cong \angle ZWU$ — 2. If two parallel lines are cut by a transversal, then their alternate interior angles are congruent.
3. $\overline{ZU} \parallel \overline{ST}$ — 3. Given
4. $\angle UST \cong \angle ZUW$ — 4. If two parallel lines are cut by a transversal, then their alternate interior angles are congruent.
5. $\triangle UST \sim \triangle WUZ$ — 5. Angle-Angle Similarity
6. $\dfrac{ZU}{ST} = \dfrac{ZW}{TU}$ — 6. Converse of the definition of similar triangles
7. $ZU \times TU = ZW \times ST$ — 7. In a proportion, the product of the means is equal to the product of the extremes.

CHAPTER 11

Practice 72

a. $y = 15$

b. $a = 20$

c. perimeter $= 35$

d. $x = 10$

e.

	Statements		Reasons
1.	$\overline{KM}$ bisects $\angle LMN$.	1.	Given
2.	$\angle KML \cong \angle KMN$	2.	Definition of an angle bisector
3.	$LK = KM$	3.	Given
4.	$\angle KLM \cong \angle KML$	4.	Base Angles Theorem
5.	$\angle KLM \cong \angle KMN$	5.	Transitive Property
6.	$\angle N \cong \angle N$	6.	Reflexive Property
7.	$\triangle NMK \sim \triangle NLM$	7.	Angle-Angle Similarity
8.	$\dfrac{LN}{MN} = \dfrac{MN}{KN}$	8.	Converse of the definition of similar triangles

Problem Set 72

1. True

2. True

3. E

4. B

5. C

6. $\dfrac{RU}{US} = \dfrac{2}{3}$; $\dfrac{TV}{VS} = \dfrac{2}{3}$; $\overline{RT}$ is parallel to $\overline{UV}$.

7. $\dfrac{US}{RS} = \dfrac{3}{5}$; $\dfrac{VS}{TS} = \dfrac{3}{5}$; $\overline{RT}$ is parallel to $\overline{UV}$.

8. $y = 20$

9. $x = 16$

10. $\angle E$

11. B

12. C

13. D

14. D

15. A

16. $x = 30$

17. $y = 6.5$

18. $x = 36$

19. perimeter $= 27$

20. perimeter $= 33$

21. 54 acrobats

22. $HI = 6$; $DJ = 8$

23.

	Statements		Reasons
1.	$\overline{DE}$ is an altitude of right $\triangle BCD$.	1.	Given
2.	$\triangle DEC \sim \triangle BDC$	2.	The altitude to the hypotenuse of a right triangle forms two triangles that are similar to each other and to the original triangle.
3.	$\dfrac{EC}{CD} = \dfrac{CD}{BC}$	3.	Converse of the definition of similar triangles
4.	$CD = BE$	4.	Given
5.	$\dfrac{EC}{BE} = \dfrac{BE}{BC}$	5.	Substitution Property

24.

	Statements		Reasons
1.	$\overline{SR}$ bisects $\angle PRQ$.	1.	Given
2.	$\angle PRS \cong \angle QRS$	2.	Definition of an angle bisector
3.	$PS = SR$	3.	Given
4.	$\angle SPR \cong \angle PRS$	4.	Base Angles Theorem
5.	$\angle SPR \cong \angle QRS$	5.	Transitive Property
6.	$\angle Q \cong \angle Q$	6.	Reflexive Property
7.	$\triangle QRS \sim \triangle QPR$	7.	Angle-Angle Similarity
8.	$\dfrac{PQ}{RQ} = \dfrac{RQ}{SQ}$	8.	Converse of the definition of similar triangles

Practice 73

a. $x = 12$

b. $PQ = 15$

c. $RT = 14$; $KM = 21$

d. 8.66

e.

	Statements		Reasons
1.	$p^2 + q^2 = m^2$	1.	Given
2.	Draw right $\triangle WRT$ with legs p and q adjacent to right $\angle R$.	2.	Definition of a right triangle
3.	$p^2 + q^2 = n^2$	3.	Pythagorean Theorem
4.	$m^2 = n^2$	4.	Substitution Property
5.	$m = n$	5.	Take the square root of both sides.
6.	$\triangle QMP \cong \triangle WRT$	6.	Side-Side-Side
7.	$\angle M \cong \angle R$	7.	C.P.C.T.C.
8.	$\angle M$ is a right angle.	8.	Congruent angles have equal measures.
9.	$\triangle QMP$ is a right triangle.	9.	Definition of a right triangle

Problem Set 73
1. True
2. True
3. A
4. D
5. D
6. B
7. E
8. 90, 72, 18
9. 77, 77, 26
10. $x = 6$
11. $x = 13$
12. $7:5$
13. $1:20$
14. $\dfrac{DL}{KD} = \dfrac{4}{5}$; $\dfrac{CM}{KC} = \dfrac{4}{5}$; Sides are divided proportionally.
15. $\dfrac{DL}{KL} = \dfrac{4}{9}$; $\dfrac{CM}{KM} = \dfrac{4}{9}$; Sides are divided proportionally.
16. $y = 120$
17. $x = 14$
18. $FH = 10$
19. E
20. A
21. $BC = 12$; $EF = 16$
22. 10.39
23.

Statements	Reasons
1. $\overline{DP}$ bisects $\angle ADS$.	1. Given
2. $m\angle ADP = m\angle PDS$	2. Definition of an angle bisector
3. $m\angle DPA > m\angle PDS$	3. The measure of an exterior angle of a triangle is greater than the measure of either of the remote interior angles.
4. $m\angle DPA > m\angle ADP$	4. Substitution Property of Inequality
5. $DA > PA$	5. If Unequal Angles, then Unequal Sides

24.

Statements	Reasons
1. $a^2 + b^2 = c^2$	1. Given
2. Draw right $\triangle EFG$ with legs a and b adjacent to right $\angle G$.	2. Definition of a right triangle
3. $a^2 + b^2 = n^2$	3. Pythagorean Theorem
4. $c^2 = n^2$	4. Substitution Property

5.	$c = n$	5. Take the square root of both sides.
6.	$\triangle ABC \cong \triangle EFG$	6. Side-Side-Side
7.	$\angle C \cong \angle G$	7. C.P.C.T.C.
8.	$\angle C$ is a right angle.	8. Congruent angles have equal measures.
9.	$\triangle ABC$ is a right triangle.	9. Definition of a right triangle

Practice 74
a. 13.44
b. $y = 2\sqrt{13}$
c. $x = 60$
d. $WX = 27$; $WZ = 21$
e.

Statements	Reasons
1. Trapezoid $ABCD$, $AL = MD$	1. Given
2. $AL + LM = MD + LM$	2. Addition Property
3. $AM = AL + LM$ and $DL = MD + LM$	3. Betweenness of Points
4. $AM = DL$	4. Substitution Property
5. $KL = KM$	5. Given
6. $m\angle KLM = m\angle KML$	6. Base Angles Theorem
7. $BM = CL$	7. Given
8. $\triangle BAM \cong \triangle CDL$	8. Side-Angle-Side
9. $BA = CD$	9. C.P.C.T.C.
10. Trapezoid $ABCD$ is isosceles.	10. Definition of an isosceles trapezoid

Problem Set 74
1. False
2. True
3. C
4. A
5. C
6. 3.32
7. 7.95
8. $? = 6$
9. $? = 17$
10. $x = 4$
11. $y = 2\sqrt{5}$
12. E
13. perimeter $= 24$
14. B
15. C
16. C
17. D

18. $x = 27$
19. $y = 40$
20. A
21. E
22. $JK = 68$; $JL = 128$
23. $ST = 75$; $TV = 25$

24.

Statements		Reasons
1.	$\Delta TPS \sim \Delta VWR$; $\overline{UR}$ bisects $\angle WRT$.	1. Given
2.	$\angle PST \cong \angle WRV$	2. Converse of the definition of similar triangles
3.	$\angle WRV \cong \angle VRP$	3. Definition of an angle bisector
4.	$\angle PST \cong \angle VRP$	4. Transitive Property
5.	$\angle TPS \cong \angle VPR$	5. Pairs of vertical angles are congruent.
6.	$\Delta TPS \sim \Delta VPR$	6. Angle-Angle Similarity

25.

Statements		Reasons
1.	Trapezoid $RSTU$, $RP = UQ$	1. Given
2.	$RP + PQ = UQ + PQ$	2. Addition Property
3.	$RQ = RP + PQ$ and $UP = UQ + PQ$	3. Betweenness of Points
4.	$RQ = UP$	4. Substitution Property
5.	$VP = VQ$	5. Given
6.	$m\angle VPQ = m\angle VQP$	6. Base Angles Theorem
7.	$SQ = TP$	7. Given
8.	$\Delta SRQ \cong \Delta TUP$	8. Side-Angle-Side
9.	$SR = TU$	9. C.P.C.T.C.
10.	Trapezoid $RSTU$ is isosceles.	10. Definition of an isosceles trapezoid

Practice 75

a. D
b. $y = 6\sqrt{2}$
c. $x = 35$
d. perimeter = 48.84
e.

Statements		Reasons
1.	Quadrilateral $JKLM$ with diagonals $\overline{MK}$ and $\overline{JL}$; $\overline{MK}$ bisects $\overline{JL}$ at O.	1. Given
2.	$\overline{JO} \cong \overline{LO}$	2. Definition of a segment bisector
3.	$\angle JOK \cong \angle LOM$	3. Pairs of vertical angles are congruent.
4.	$\angle LJK \cong \angle JLM$	4. Given
5.	$\Delta JOK \cong \Delta LOM$	5. Angle-Side-Angle
6.	$\overline{JK} \cong \overline{ML}$	6. C.P.C.T.C.
7.	$\overline{JK} \parallel \overline{ML}$	7. If two lines form congruent alternate interior angles with a transversal, then the lines are parallel.
8.	$JKLM$ is a parallelogram.	8. If one pair of sides is both parallel and congruent, then a quadrilateral is a parallelogram.

Problem Set 75

1. False
2. True
3. D
4. C
5. A
6. E
7. C
8. Yes
9. No
10. $14\sqrt{2}$
11. $QE = 7$, $QW = 7\sqrt{2}$
12. B
13. $y = 5\sqrt{2}$
14. $x = 5\sqrt{6}$
15. $y = 90$, $z = 125$
16. $x = 85$
17. $x = 105$
18. B
19. D
20. $m\angle L = 32$, $PR = 6$
21. 12, 15
22. perimeter = 48.16

23.

Statements		Reasons
1.	Parallelogram $DEFG$	1. Given
2.	$\overline{DE} \parallel \overline{GF}$ and $\overline{DK} \parallel \overline{MF}$	2. Definition of a parallelogram
3.	$\angle GLK \cong \angle ENM$	3. If two parallel lines are cut by a transversal, then their alternate exterior

			angles are congruent.
4.	$\angle M \cong \angle K$	4.	If two parallel lines are cut by a transversal, then their alternate interior angles are congruent.
5.	$\overline{KL} \cong \overline{MN}$	5.	Given
6.	$\triangle KGL \cong \triangle MEN$	6.	Angle-Side-Angle
7.	$\overline{GL} \cong \overline{EN}$	7.	C.P.C.T.C.

24.

	Statements		Reasons
1.	Quadrilateral $QRST$ with diagonals $\overline{QS}$ and $\overline{RT}$; $\overline{RT}$ bisects $\overline{QS}$ at P.	1.	Given
2.	$\overline{QP} \cong \overline{SP}$	2.	Definition of a segment bisector
3.	$\angle RPS \cong \angle TPQ$	3.	Pairs of vertical angles are congruent.
4.	$\angle SQT \cong \angle RSQ$	4.	Given
5.	$\triangle RPS \cong \triangle TPQ$	5.	Angle-Side-Angle
6.	$\overline{RS} \cong \overline{QT}$	6.	C.P.C.T.C.
7.	$\overline{RS} \parallel \overline{QT}$	7.	If two lines form congruent alternate interior angles with a transversal, then the lines are parallel.
8.	$QRST$ is a parallelogram.	8.	If one pair of sides is both parallel and congruent, then a quadrilateral is a parallelogram.

Practice 76

a. $7\sqrt{2}$; 9.87
b. 8 inches
c. B
d. 13.93 feet
e. Statements

	Statements		Reasons
1.	$\overline{KJ} \perp \overline{JM}$, $\overline{MN} \perp \overline{KN}$, $\overline{LN} \perp \overline{JM}$	1.	Given
2.	$\angle KJO$, $\angle ONM$, and $\angle NLM$ are right angles.	2.	Perpendicular lines intersect to form right angles.

3.	$\angle KJO \cong \angle ONM$	3.	All right angles are congruent.
4.	$\angle JOK \cong \angle NOM$	4.	Pairs of vertical angles are congruent.
5.	$\triangle JOK \sim \triangle NOM$	5.	Angle-Angle Similarity
6.	$\angle K \cong \angle M$	6.	Converse of the definition of similar triangles
7.	$\angle KJO \cong \angle NLM$	7.	All right angles are congruent.
8.	$\triangle KJO \sim \triangle MLN$	8.	Angle-Angle Similarity

Problem Set 76

1. True
2. True
3. E
4. C
5. A
6. $4\sqrt{2}$, 5.64
7. $3\sqrt{5}$; 6.72
8. ? = 26
9. ? = $3\sqrt{3}$
10. 7 inches
11. 4 inches
12. 1 : 2
13. 7 : 6
14. perimeter = 33.74
15. perimeter = 42.10
16. $x = 78$
17. $y = 6$
18. A
19. D
20. D
21. 15 feet
22. 12.53 feet

23.

	Statements		Reasons
1.	$\overline{LP} \cong \overline{LK}$	1.	Given
2.	$\angle P \cong \angle LKM$	2.	Base Angles Theorem
3.	$\overline{PK}$ bisects $\angle LKN$.	3.	Given
4.	$\angle LKM \cong \angle NKM$	4.	Definition of an angle bisector
5.	$\angle P \cong \angle NKM$	5.	Transitive Property
6.	$\angle LMP \cong \angle KMN$	6.	Pairs of vertical angles are congruent.
7.	$\triangle LMP \sim \triangle NMK$	7.	Angle-Angle Similarity

8. $\dfrac{LP}{NK} = \dfrac{MP}{MK}$ | 8. Converse of the definition of similar triangles

24.

Statements	Reasons
1. $\overline{AD} \perp \overline{DE}$, $\overline{AB} \perp \overline{BE}$, $\overline{BF} \perp \overline{AD}$	1. Given
2. $\angle BFA$, $\angle ABC$, and $\angle CDE$ are right angles.	2. Perpendicular lines intersect to form right angles.
3. $\angle ABC \cong \angle CDE$	3. All right angles are congruent.
4. $\angle BCA \cong \angle DCE$	4. Pairs of vertical angles are congruent.
5. $\triangle BCA \sim \triangle DCE$	5. Angle-Angle Similarity
6. $\angle A \cong \angle E$	6. Converse of the definition of similar triangles
7. $\angle BFA \cong \angle CDE$	7. All right angles are congruent.
8. $\triangle FAB \sim \triangle DEC$	8. Angle-Angle Similarity

Practice 77
a. E
b. perimeter = 90
c. $x = 4$
d. 55 ringtones
e.

Statements	Reasons
1. $\angle JML$ and $\angle KNL$ are complements of $\angle JMN$.	1. Given
2. $\angle JML \cong \angle KNL$	2. Complements of the same angle are congruent.
3. $\overline{JL} \perp \overline{ML}$ and $\overline{KL} \perp \overline{NL}$	3. Given
4. $\angle JLM$ and $\angle KLN$ are right angles.	4. Perpendicular lines intersect to form right angles.
5. $\angle JLM \cong \angle KLN$	5. All right angles are congruent.
6. $\overline{JM} \cong \overline{KN}$	6. Given
7. $\triangle JML \cong \triangle KNL$	7. Angle-Angle-Side
8. $\overline{ML} \cong \overline{NL}$	8. C.P.C.T.C.
9. $\triangle LMN$ is isosceles.	9. Definition of an isosceles triangle

Problem Set 77
1. True
2. True
3. C
4. B
5. E
6. $\dfrac{DE}{DF}$
7. $\dfrac{EF}{DE}$
8. $3\sqrt{5}$
9. D
10. $? = 8$; $x = 15$
11. $? = 20$; $x = 15$
12. $FS = 20$, $QU = 24$
13. perimeter = 96
14. $x = 2\sqrt{21}$
15. $y = 2\sqrt{70}$
16. B
17. B
18. $x = 20$
19. $y = 50$
20. $z = 5$
21. 24 hits
22. 60 pieces of candy

23.

Statements	Reasons
1. T is the midpoint of $\overline{PS}$.	1. Given
2. $PT = TS$	2. Definition of a midpoint
3. $\angle P \cong \angle S$	3. Given
4. $\overline{VP} \cong \overline{VS}$	4. Converse of the Base Angles Theorem
5. $\triangle TVP \cong \triangle TVS$	5. Side-Angle-Side

24.

Statements	Reasons
1. $\angle BCE$ and $\angle DFE$ are complements of $\angle BCF$.	1. Given
2. $\angle BCE \cong \angle DFE$	2. Complements of the same angle are congruent.
3. $\overline{BC} \perp \overline{BE}$ and $\overline{DE} \perp \overline{DF}$	3. Given
4. $\angle CBE$ and $\angle FDE$ are right angles.	4. Perpendicular lines intersect to form right angles.
5. $\angle CBE \cong \angle FDE$	5. All right angles are congruent.
6. $\overline{BC} \cong \overline{DF}$	6. Given

7.	$\triangle BCE \cong \triangle DFE$	7.	Angle-Side-Angle
8.	$\overline{CE} \cong \overline{FE}$	8.	C.P.C.T.C.
9.	$\triangle CEF$ is isosceles.	9.	Definition of an isosceles triangle

Practice 78

a. perimeter $= 30$
b. 0.7813
c. $y = 26$
d. $x = 6$
e. Statements

Statements		Reasons
1. $CDEF$ is a parallelogram.		1. Given
2. $\overline{CD} \cong \overline{FE}$ and $\overline{CF} \cong \overline{DE}$		2. Opposite sides of a parallelogram are congruent.
3. $\overline{CD} \parallel \overline{FE}$ and $\overline{CF} \parallel \overline{DE}$		3. Definition of a parallelogram
4. $\angle CDH \cong \angle EFG$ and $\angle CFG \cong \angle EDH$		4. If two parallel lines are cut by a transversal, then their alternate interior angles are congruent.
5. $\overline{FG} \cong \overline{DH}$		5. Given
6. $\triangle DCH \cong \triangle FEG$ and $\triangle CFG \cong \triangle EDH$		6. Side-Angle-Side
7. $\overline{CH} \cong \overline{EG}$ and $\overline{CG} \cong \overline{EH}$		7. C.P.C.T.C.
8. $CGEH$ is a parallelogram.		8. If both pairs of opposite sides of a quadrilateral are congruent, then it is a parallelogram.

Problem Set 78

1. True
2. False
3. D
4. A
5. C
6. $720°$
7. $1,080°$
8. $\overline{PR}$ or $\overline{RP}$
9. B
10. $? = 7\sqrt{5}$
11. $? = 3\sqrt{21}$
12. perimeter $= 18$
13. perimeter $= 42$
14. 0.4040

15. 2.4751
16. $x = 17.32$
17. $y = 22.23$
18. $x = 45$
19. $y = 50$
20. $x = 9$
21. 12.21 feet
22. 2.55 miles
23. Statements

Statements	Reasons
1. $\overline{SR}$ divides $\overline{PT}$ and $\overline{PQ}$ proportionally.	1. Given
2. $\overline{SR} \parallel \overline{TQ}$	2. If a line intersects two sides of a triangle and divides those sides proportionally, then the line is parallel to the third side.
3. $\angle SRQ$ and $\angle RQT$ are supplementary.	3. If two parallel lines are cut by a transversal, then their interior angles on the same side of the transversal are supplementary.
4. $m\angle SRQ + m\angle RQT = 180$	4. Definition of supplementary angles

24. Statements

Statements	Reasons
1. $HIJK$ is a parallelogram.	1. Given
2. $\overline{HI} \cong \overline{KJ}$ and $\overline{HK} \cong \overline{IJ}$	2. Opposite sides of a parallelogram are congruent.
3. $\overline{HI} \parallel \overline{KJ}$ and $\overline{HK} \parallel \overline{IJ}$	3. Definition of a parallelogram
4. $\angle LHI \cong \angle MJK$ and $\angle LHK \cong \angle MJI$	4. If two parallel lines are cut by a transversal, then their alternate interior angles are congruent.
5. $\overline{HL} \cong \overline{JM}$	5. Given
6. $\triangle HLI \cong \triangle JMK$ and $\triangle HLK \cong \triangle JMI$	6. Side-Angle-Side
7. $\overline{LK} \cong \overline{MI}$ and $\overline{MK} \cong \overline{LI}$	7. C.P.C.T.C.
8. $LIMK$ is a parallelogram.	8. If both pairs of opposite sides of a quadrilateral are congruent, then it is a parallelogram.

Practice 79

a. $4\sqrt{13}$
b. $x = 44$
c. $y = 2\sqrt{22}$
d. 10.50 feet
e. Statements

	Statements		Reasons
1.	$\overline{AB}$ and $\overline{CD}$ bisect each other at point F.	1.	Given
2.	$\overline{AF} \cong \overline{FB}$ and $\overline{CF} \cong \overline{FD}$	2.	Definition of a segment bisector
3.	$\angle AFC \cong \angle BFD$	3.	Pairs of vertical angles are congruent.
4.	$\triangle CAF \cong \triangle DBF$	4.	Side-Angle-Side
5.	$\angle C \cong \angle D$ and $\overline{CA} \cong \overline{BD}$	5.	C.P.C.T.C.
6.	$\angle CAE \cong \angle GBD$	6.	Given
7.	$\triangle CAE \cong \triangle DBG$	7.	Angle-Side-Angle
8.	$\overline{AE} \cong \overline{GB}$	8.	C.P.C.T.C.

Problem Set 79

1. True
2. True
3. A
4. B
5. E
6. $6\sqrt{2}$; 8.46
7. $5\sqrt{7}$; 13.25
8. 0.3907
9. 0.2250
10. 6.3138
11. 52
12. $5\sqrt{17}$
13. C
14. C
15. $23\sqrt{2}$
16. $SM = 6$; $TM = 6\sqrt{3}$
17. $x = 8$
18. $y = 113$
19. $y = 4\sqrt{51}$
20. 31.89 feet
21. 95.08 miles
22. 26.39 feet
23. Statements

	Statements		Reasons
1.	$ERDT$ is a trapezoid.	1.	Given
2.	$\overline{RD} \parallel \overline{ET}$	2.	Definition of a trapezoid
3.	$\angle RDE \cong \angle TED$	3.	If two parallel lines are cut by a transversal, then their alternate interior angles are congruent.
4.	$\angle RPD \cong \angle TPE$	4.	Pairs of vertical angles are congruent.
5.	$\triangle RPD \sim \triangle TPE$	5.	Angle-Angle Similarity
6.	$\dfrac{DP}{EP} = \dfrac{RP}{TP}$	6.	Converse of the definition of similar triangles
7.	$DP \times TP = RP \times EP$	7.	In a proportion, the product of the means is equal to the product of the extremes.

24. Statements

	Statements		Reasons
1.	$\overline{IJ}$ and $\overline{KL}$ bisect each other at point N.	1.	Given
2.	$\overline{IN} \cong \overline{NJ}$ and $\overline{KN} \cong \overline{NL}$	2.	Definition of a segment bisector
3.	$\angle INL \cong \angle JNK$	3.	Pairs of vertical angles are congruent.
4.	$\triangle LIN \cong \triangle KJN$	4.	Side-Angle-Side
5.	$\angle K \cong \angle L$ and $\overline{LI} \cong \overline{JK}$	5.	C.P.C.T.C.
6.	$\angle LIO \cong \angle MJK$	6.	Given
7.	$\triangle LIO \cong \triangle KJM$	7.	Angle-Side-Angle
8.	$\overline{IO} \cong \overline{MJ}$	8.	C.P.C.T.C.

Practice 80

a. 30, 60, 90
b. perimeter = 19.64
c. $x = 55$
d. 28.97 feet
e. Statements

	Statements		Reasons
1.	$\overline{PQ} \cong \overline{PT}$, $\overline{OQ} \cong \overline{OT}$	1.	Given
2.	$\overline{OP} \cong \overline{OP}$	2.	Reflexive Property
3.	$\triangle OPQ \cong \triangle OPT$	3.	Side-Side-Side
4.	$\angle OQP \cong \angle OTP$	4.	C.P.C.T.C.
5.	$\angle OQP$ and $\angle RQO$ are supplementary; $\angle OTP$ and $\angle STO$ are supplementary.	5.	If two angles are a linear pair, then they are supplementary.
6.	$\angle RQO \cong \angle STO$	6.	If two angles are supplementary to congruent angles, then they are congruent.

	Statements		Reasons
7.	$\angle ROQ \cong \angle SOT$	7.	Pairs of vertical angles are congruent.
8.	$\Delta ROQ \cong \Delta SOT$	8.	Angle-Side-Angle
9.	$\overline{RO} \cong \overline{SO}$	9.	C.P.C.T.C.
10.	ΔRSO is isosceles.	10.	Definition of an isosceles triangle

Problem Set 80

1. True
2. True
3. C
4. D
5. B
6. A
7. C
8. $\dfrac{UV}{UW}$
9. $\dfrac{VW}{UV}$
10. 98, 41, 41
11. 90, 60, 30
12. 0.75
13. 0.80
14. perimeter = 40.95
15. perimeter = 29.05
16. $? = 6$; $x = 11.25$
17. $? = 15$; $x = 11.25$
18. $x = 5\sqrt{2}$
19. $x = 84$
20. $y = 16.30$
21. 15.62 feet
22. 14.85 feet

23.

	Statements		Reasons
1.	$\ell \parallel m$	1.	Given
2.	$\angle ACB \cong \angle CBE$	2.	If two parallel lines are cut by a transversal, then their alternate interior angles are congruent.
3.	$\overline{CB}$ bisects $\angle ABE$.	3.	Given
4.	$\angle ABC \cong \angle CBE$	4.	Definition of an angle bisector
5.	$\angle ACB \cong \angle ABC$	5.	Transitive Property
6.	$\overline{AB} \cong \overline{AC}$	6.	Converse of the Base Angles Theorem
7.	D is the midpoint of $\overline{CB}$.	7.	Given

	Statements		Reasons
8.	$\overline{CD} \cong \overline{DB}$	8.	Definition of a midpoint
9.	$\Delta ADC \cong \Delta ADB$	9.	Side-Angle-Side
10.	$\angle BAD \cong \angle DAC$	10.	C.P.C.T.C.
11.	$\overline{AD}$ bisects $\angle BAC$.	11.	Definition of an angle bisector

24.

	Statements		Reasons
1.	$\overline{KH} \cong \overline{LH}$, $\overline{JK} \cong \overline{JL}$	1.	Given
2.	$\overline{JH} \cong \overline{JH}$	2.	Reflexive Property
3.	$\Delta JKH \cong \Delta JLH$	3.	Side-Side-Side
4.	$\angle JKH \cong \angle JLH$	4.	C.P.C.T.C.
5.	$\angle JKH$ and $\angle FKJ$ are supplementary; $\angle JLH$ and $\angle GLJ$ are supplementary.	5.	If two angles are a linear pair, then they are supplementary.
6.	$\angle FKJ \cong \angle GLJ$	6.	If two angles are supplementary to congruent angles, then they are congruent.
7.	$\angle FJK \cong \angle GJL$	7.	Pairs of vertical angles are congruent.
8.	$\Delta FJK \cong \Delta GJL$	8.	Angle-Side-Angle
9.	$\overline{FJ} \cong \overline{GJ}$	9.	C.P.C.T.C.
10.	ΔFGJ is isosceles.	10.	Definition of an isosceles triangle

CHAPTER 12

Practice 81

a. $1\frac{1}{2}$ or $\frac{3}{2}$ inches

b. $x = 8$

c. $\tan x = 1$

d. 156 cars

e.

	Statements		Reasons
1.	$\triangle MNO \cong \triangle QPO$	1.	Given
2.	$\overline{NO} \cong \overline{PO}$ and $\overline{MN} \cong \overline{QP}$, or $NO = PO$ and $MN = QP$	2.	C.P.C.T.C.
3.	$LM = LQ$	3.	Given
4.	$LM + MN = LQ + QP$	4.	Addition Property
5.	$LN = LM + MN$ and $LP = LQ + QP$	5.	Betweenness of Points
6.	$\overline{LN} \cong \overline{LP}$ or $LN = LP$	6.	Substitution Property
7.	$\overline{LO} \cong \overline{LO}$	7.	Reflexive Property
8.	$\triangle LNO \cong \triangle LPO$	8.	Side-Side-Side

Problem Set 81

1. True
2. True
3. B
4. C
5. A
6. B
7. E
8. 0.9703
9. 0.9703
10. $21\sqrt{2}$
11. $1\frac{1}{3}$ or $\frac{4}{3}$ inches
12. $7\sqrt{2}$
13. $JL = 13$; $KL = 13\sqrt{3}$
14. C
15. E
16. $\angle F$
17. B
18. $x = 3$
19. $y = 67$
20. $\tan x = 1$
21. 95 lipstick wearers
22. 256 cars

23.	Statements		Reasons
1.	$\dfrac{QT}{QW} = \dfrac{QS}{QV}$	1.	Given
2.	$\angle SQT \cong \angle VQW$	2.	Reflexive Property
3.	$\triangle SQT \sim \triangle VQW$	3.	Side-Angle-Side Similarity
4.	$\angle VWQ \cong \angle STQ$	4.	Converse of the definition of similar triangles
5.	$\angle STQ \cong \angle RPQ$	5.	Given
6.	$\angle VWQ \cong \angle RPQ$	6.	Transitive Property
7.	$\overline{PR} \parallel \overline{VW}$	7.	If two lines form congruent alternate interior angles with a transversal, then the lines are parallel.

24.	Statements		Reasons
1.	$\triangle BCF \cong \triangle BHG$	1.	Given
2.	$\overline{BC} \cong \overline{BH}$ and $\overline{CF} \cong \overline{HG}$, or $BC = BH$ and $CF = HG$	2.	C.P.C.T.C.
3.	$FE = GE$	3.	Given
4.	$CF + FE = HG + GE$	4.	Addition Property
5.	$CE = CF + FE$ and $HE = HG + GE$	5.	Betweenness of Points
6.	$CE = HE$ or $\overline{CE} \cong \overline{HE}$	6.	Substitution Property
7.	$\overline{BE} \cong \overline{BE}$	7.	Reflexive Property
8.	$\triangle BCE \cong \triangle BHE$	8.	Side-Side-Side

Practice 82

a. E

b. diameter $= 10$

c. $x = 5.66$

d. 2.79 ft.

e.

	Statements		Reasons
1.	$\overline{NP} \perp \overline{LM}$ and $\overline{RP} \perp \overline{SQ}$ in $\odot P$	1.	Given
2.	$\angle PNM$ and $\angle PRQ$ are right angles.	2.	Perpendicular lines intersect to form right angles.
3.	Draw radii $\overline{PM}$ and $\overline{PQ}$; $\overline{PM} \cong \overline{PQ}$	3.	All radii of the same circle are congruent.
4.	$\triangle PNM$ and $\triangle PRQ$ are right triangles.	4.	Definition of a right triangle

	Statements		Reasons
5.	$\overline{NP} \cong \overline{RP}$	5.	Given
6.	$\triangle PNM \cong \triangle PRQ$	6.	Hypotenuse-Leg
7.	$MN = QR$	7.	C.P.C.T.C.
8.	$\overline{NP}$ bisects chord $\overline{LM}$ and $\overline{RP}$ bisects chord $\overline{QS}$.	8.	If a line through the center of a circle is perpendicular to a chord, it also bisects the chord.
9.	$MN = NL$ and $QR = RS$	9.	Definition of a segment bisector
10.	$NL = RS$	10.	Transitive Property
11.	$MN + NL = QR + RS$	11.	Addition Property
12.	$ML = MN + NL$ and $QS = QR + RS$	12.	Betweenness of Points
13.	$ML = QS$ or $\overline{ML} \cong \overline{QS}$	13.	Substitution Property

Problem Set 82

1. True
2. True
3. D
4. B
5. E
6. C
7. D
8. A
9. A
10. D
11. $y = 12.00$
12. $x = 21.63$
13. $CD = 9$; $DF = 9\sqrt{3}$
14. diameter $= 20$
15. perimeter $= 116$
16. perimeter $= 92$
17. A
18. C
19. $x = 5$
20. $y = 5\sqrt{7}$
21. $x = 6.63$
22. 187 feet
23. 4.41 feet

24.

	Statements		Reasons
1.	$\overline{QT} \perp \overline{PR}$ and $\overline{RU} \perp \overline{TS}$	1.	Given
2.	$\angle TQP$ and $\angle RUS$ are right angles.	2.	Perpendicular lines intersect to form right angles.
3.	$\angle TQP \cong \angle RUS$	3.	All right angles are congruent.
4.	$PRST$ is a parallelogram.	4.	Given
5.	$\angle TPQ \cong \angle RSU$	5.	Opposite angles of a parallelogram are congruent.
6.	$\overline{PT} \cong \overline{SR}$	6.	Opposite sides of a parallelogram are congruent.
7.	$\triangle PTQ \cong \triangle SRU$	7.	Angle-Angle-Side
8.	$\overline{PQ} \cong \overline{SU}$	8.	C.P.C.T.C.

25.

	Statements		Reasons
1.	$\overline{AB} \perp \overline{FO}$ and $\overline{CD} \perp \overline{EO}$ in $\odot O$	1.	Given
2.	$\angle AFO$ and $\angle CEO$ are right angles.	2.	Perpendicular lines intersect to form right angles.
3.	Draw radii $\overline{AO}$ and $\overline{CO}$; $\overline{AO} \cong \overline{CO}$	3.	All radii of the same circle are congruent.
4.	$\triangle AFO$ and $\triangle CEO$ are right triangles.	4.	Definition of a right triangle
5.	$\overline{FO} \cong \overline{EO}$	5.	Given
6.	$\triangle AFO \cong \triangle CEO$	6.	Hypotenuse-Leg
7.	$AF = CE$	7.	C.P.C.T.C.
8.	$\overline{FO}$ bisects chord $\overline{AB}$ and $\overline{EO}$ bisects chord $\overline{CD}$.	8.	If a line through the center of a circle is perpendicular to a chord, it also bisects the chord.
9.	$AF = FB$ and $CE = ED$	9.	Definition of a segment bisector
10.	$FB = ED$	10.	Transitive Property
11.	$AF + FB = CE + ED$	11.	Addition Property
12.	$AB = AF + FB$ and $CD = CE + ED$	12.	Betweenness of Points
13.	$AB = CD$ or $\overline{AB} \cong \overline{CD}$	13.	Substitution Property

Practice 83

a. $? = 6.25$; $x = 11.79$
b. $RS = 25$
c. $x = 9\sqrt{2}$

d. $m\angle H = 73$, $FG = 44$

e. $\overline{KL} \perp \overleftrightarrow{LW}$ at point L on $\odot K$ (Given). Assume $\overleftrightarrow{LW}$ is not tangent to $\odot K$. That means it must intersect $\odot K$ at another point, W. Since $\overline{KW}$ is the hypotenuse of $\triangle KLW$, $KW > KL$. But if W is on the circle, $\overline{KW}$ should be a radius and equal to $\overline{KL}$. The assumption that $\overleftrightarrow{LW}$ is not a tangent must be false. Therefore, $\overleftrightarrow{LW}$ has to be tangent to $\odot K$.

25. $\overline{OP} \perp \overleftrightarrow{RP}$ at point P on $\odot O$ (Given). Assume $\overleftrightarrow{RP}$ is not tangent to $\odot O$. That means it must intersect $\odot O$ at another point, R. Since $\overline{OR}$ is the hypotenuse of $\triangle OPR$, $OR > OP$. But if R is on the circle, $\overline{OR}$ should be a radius and equal to $\overline{OP}$. The assumption that $\overleftrightarrow{RP}$ is not a tangent must be false. Therefore, $\overleftrightarrow{RP}$ has to be tangent to $\odot O$.

Problem Set 83

1. True
2. False
3. D
4. D
5. B
6. $? = 7.42$
7. $? = 9.63$; $x = 11.91$
8. $? = 3.58$; $x = 9.34$
9. C
10. C
11. 45, 45, 90
12. 30, 30, 120
13. $\overline{GH}$ or $\overline{HG}$
14. $BN = 4$
15. perimeter = 204
16. $IJ = 15$
17. A
18. C
19. $x = 100$
20. $y = 72$
21. $x = 12\sqrt{2}$
22. 63, 27
23. $m\angle S = 116$, $PT = 42$
24.

	Statements		Reasons
1.	Rectangle $ABCD$ and $\odot P$	1.	Given
2.	$\angle PCD$ is a right angle.	2.	Definition of a rectangle
3.	$\overline{PC} \perp \overline{DC}$	3.	Definition of perpendicular lines
4.	$\overline{DC}$ is tangent to $\odot P$.	4.	If a radius is perpendicular to a line at the point where the line intersects a circle, then the line is a tangent line.

Practice 84

a. $m\overarc{FG} = 55$
b. base = 8.9, legs = 10.9
c. $y = 5\sqrt{6}$
d. 30.47 feet
e.

	Statements		Reasons
1.	$\overline{JM} \cong \overline{IJ}$	1.	Given
2.	$\angle IMJ \cong \angle JIK$	2.	Base Angles Theorem
3.	$\angle IMJ \cong \angle LMK$	3.	Pairs of vertical angles are congruent.
4.	$\angle JIK \cong \angle LMK$	4.	Transitive Property
5.	$\overline{MK}$ bisects $\angle JKL$.	5.	Given
6.	$\angle JKI \cong \angle MKL$	6.	Definition of an angle bisector
7.	$\triangle KML \sim \triangle KIJ$	7.	Angle-Angle Similarity
8.	$\dfrac{KI}{KM} = \dfrac{IJ}{ML}$	8.	Converse of the definition of similar triangles
9.	$KI \times ML = KM \times IJ$	9.	In a proportion, the product of the means is equal to the product of the extremes.

Problem Set 84

1. False
2. True
3. E
4. B
5. A
6. A
7. C
8. $m\angle ROS = 35$
9. $m\overarc{PQ} = 30$
10. 0.4961
11. $JO = 6.7$
12. $HJ = 5\sqrt{3}$
13. base = 18.88, legs = 16.89
14. perimeter = 24

15. perimeter = 42.69

16. $x = 6\sqrt{6}$

17. $y = 12$

18. $x = 9$

19. B

20. D

21. 13.01 inches

22. 59.64 feet

23.

Statements	Reasons
1. $\overline{JK}$ is tangent to $\odot P$ at J and to $\odot O$ at K.	1. Given
2. $\overline{PJ} \perp \overline{JK}$ and $\overline{KO} \perp \overline{JK}$	2. If a radius is drawn to the point of tangency of a tangent line, then the radius is perpendicular to the tangent line.
3. $\angle PJK$ and $\angle OKM$ are right angles.	3. Perpendicular lines intersect to form right angles.
4. $\angle PJK \cong \angle OKM$	4. All right angles are congruent.
5. $\overline{PJ} \parallel \overline{KO}$	5. If two lines form congruent alternate interior angles with a transversal, then the lines are parallel.
6. $\angle 1 \cong \angle 2$	6. If two parallel lines are cut by a transversal, then their alternate interior angles are congruent.

24.

Statements	Reasons
1. $\overline{BE} \cong \overline{AB}$	1. Given
2. $\angle AEB \cong \angle BAC$	2. Base Angles Theorem
3. $\angle AEB \cong \angle DEC$	3. Pairs of vertical angles are congruent.
4. $\angle BAC \cong \angle DEC$	4. Transitive Property
5. $\overline{EC}$ bisects $\angle BCD$.	5. Given
6. $\angle BCA \cong \angle ECD$	6. Definition of an angle bisector
7. $\triangle CED \sim \triangle CAB$	7. Angle-Angle Similarity
8. $\dfrac{CA}{CE} = \dfrac{AB}{ED}$	8. Converse of the definition of similar triangles

9. $CA \times ED = CE \times AB$	9. In a proportion, the product of the means is equal to the product of the extremes.

Practice 85

a. $m\overset{\frown}{SP} = 97$

b. $\ell\overset{\frown}{LMN} = 44\pi$

c. $XZ = 16$

d. $y = 2.98$

e.

Statements	Reasons
1. $\overline{SP}$ is tangent to $\odot O$ at S and $\overline{RQ}$ is tangent to $\odot O$ at R.	1. Given
2. $\overline{OS} \perp \overline{SP}$ and $\overline{OR} \perp \overline{RQ}$	2. A radius drawn to a tangent point is perpendicular to its tangent line.
3. $\angle PRQ$ and $\angle PSO$ are right angles.	3. Perpendicular lines intersect to form right angles.
4. $\angle PRQ \cong \angle PSO$	4. All right angles are congruent.
5. $\angle P \cong \angle P$	5. Reflexive Property
6. $\triangle QRP \sim \triangle OSP$	6. Angle-Angle Similarity

Problem Set 85

1. True

2. True

3. D

4. A

5. D

6. $m\overset{\frown}{GD} = 120$

7. $m\angle COF = 154$

8. $m\overset{\frown}{CD} = 129$

9. B

10. $\ell\overset{\frown}{BC} = 20\pi$

11. $\ell\overset{\frown}{KPL} = 23\pi$

12. $3\sqrt{2}$

13. $9\sqrt{3}$

14. $DF = 20$

15. $m\angle J = 29$, $m\angle H = 63$, $m\angle N = 88$

16. $x = 25$

17. $y = 20$

18. $y = 4.61$

19. E

20. C
21. 132 oarfish
22. 187 points
23. Statements / Reasons

#	Statements	#	Reasons
1.	$\overline{HJ} \perp \overline{JK}$ and $\overline{JL} \perp \overline{HK}$	1.	Given
2.	$\angle HJK$ is a right angle.	2.	Perpendicular lines intersect to form right angles.
3.	ΔHJK is a right triangle.	3.	Definition of a right triangle
4.	$\overline{JL}$ is an altitude of ΔHJK.	4.	Definition of an altitude
5.	$\Delta HJK \sim \Delta HLJ$	5.	The altitude to the hypotenuse of a right triangle forms two triangles that are similar to each other and to the original triangle.
6.	$\dfrac{HL}{HJ} = \dfrac{HJ}{HK}$	6.	Converse of the definition of similar triangles
7.	$HL \times HK = (HJ)^2$	7.	The product of the means equals the product of the extremes.
8.	$(HJ)^2 + (JK)^2 = (HK)^2$	8.	Pythagorean Theorem
9.	$(HJ)^2 = (HK)^2 - (JK)^2$	9.	Subtraction property
10.	$(HK)^2 - (JK)^2 = HL \times HK$	10.	Substitution Property

24. Statements / Reasons

#	Statements	#	Reasons
1.	$\overline{DH}$ is tangent to $\odot O$ at D and $\overline{FG}$ is tangent to $\odot O$ at F.	1.	Given
2.	$\overline{FG} \perp \overline{HO}$ and $\overline{OD} \perp \overline{DH}$	2.	A radius drawn to a tangent point is perpendicular to its tangent line.
3.	$\angle HFG$ and $\angle HDO$ are right angles.	3.	Perpendicular lines intersect to form right angles.
4.	$\angle HFG \cong \angle HDO$	4.	All right angles are congruent.
5.	$\angle H \cong \angle H$	5.	Reflexive Property
6.	$\Delta GFH \sim \Delta ODH$	6.	Angle-Angle Similarity

Practice 86

a. $m\widehat{HIF} = 203$
b. $\ell\widehat{JK} = 7.57$
c. $y = 15.39$
d. 1.78 miles
e. Statements / Reasons

#	Statements	#	Reasons
1.	Draw radii $\overline{OP}$ and $\overline{OR}$.	1.	Two points determine a line.
2.	$\overline{OP} \cong \overline{OR}$	2.	All radii of the same circle are congruent.
3.	$\overline{QS} \perp \overline{PR}$ in $\odot O$	3.	Given
4.	$\angle OTP$ and $\angle OTR$ are right angles.	4.	Perpendicular lines intersect to form right angles.
5.	ΔOTP and ΔOTR are right triangles.	5.	Definition of a right triangle
6.	$\overline{OT} \cong \overline{OT}$	6.	Reflexive Property
7.	$\Delta OTP \cong \Delta OTR$	7.	Hypotenuse-Leg
8.	$\angle POQ \cong \angle ROQ$	8.	C.P.C.T.C.
9.	$m\angle POQ = m\widehat{PQ}$ and $m\angle ROQ = m\widehat{RQ}$	9.	The degree measure of a minor arc is the measure of its central angle.
10.	$\widehat{PQ} \cong \widehat{RQ}$	10.	Substitution Property

Problem Set 86

1. True
2. False
3. C
4. E
5. B
6. C
7. E
8. $m\angle BOC = 109$
9. $m\widehat{CDA} = 199$
10. $\ell\widehat{WV} = 11.15$
11. $\ell\widehat{CD} = 35.88$
12. $x = 4.90$
13. $y = 9.38$
14. $CE = 48$; $RS = 21$
15. perimeter = 119
16. perimeter = 35.21
17. perimeter = 58.33
18. $x = 104$
19. $x = 15\sqrt{3}$

20. $y = 36.93$
21. 171.92 feet
22. 2.92 miles

23.

Statements	Reasons
1. $OP > PR$ in $\odot O$	1. Given
2. $m\angle ORP > m\angle POR$	2. If Unequal Sides, then Unequal Angles
3. $m\angle QOR > m\angle ORP$	3. Exterior Angle Inequality Theorem
4. $m\angle QOR > m\angle POR$	4. Transitive Property of Inequality
5. $m\angle QOR = m\overarc{QR}$ and $m\angle POR = m\overarc{PR}$	5. The degree measure of a minor arc is the measure of its central angle.
6. $m\overarc{QR} > m\overarc{PR}$	6. Substitution Property

24.

Statements	Reasons
1. Draw radii $\overline{OK}$ and $\overline{OL}$.	1. Two points determine a line.
2. $\overline{OK} \cong \overline{OL}$	2. All radii of the same circle are congruent.
3. $\overline{IJ} \perp \overline{KL}$ in $\odot O$	3. Given
4. $\angle ONK$ and $\angle ONL$ are right angles.	4. Perpendicular lines intersect to form right angles.
5. $\triangle ONK$ and $\triangle ONL$ are right triangles.	5. Definition of a right triangle
6. $\overline{ON} \cong \overline{ON}$	6. Reflexive Property
7. $\triangle ONK \cong \triangle ONL$	7. Hypotenuse-Leg
8. $\angle KOI \cong \angle LOI$	8. C.P.C.T.C.
9. $m\angle KOI = m\overarc{KI}$ and $m\angle LOI = m\overarc{IL}$	9. The degree measure of a minor arc is the measure of its central angle.
10. $\overarc{KI} \cong \overarc{IL}$	10. Substitution Property

Practice 87

a. $m\overarc{EG} = 24$
b. $\ell\overarc{DFE} = 94.2$
c. perimeter $= 8\sqrt{3}$
d. $x = 57$
e.

Statements	Reasons
1. $m\overarc{IJK} = m\overarc{LKJ}$	1. Given

Statements	Reasons
2. $m\overarc{IJ} + m\overarc{JK} = m\overarc{IJK}$ and $m\overarc{JK} + m\overarc{KL} = m\overarc{LKJ}$	2. Arc Addition Postulate
3. $m\overarc{IJ} + m\overarc{JK} = m\overarc{JK} + m\overarc{KL}$	3. Substitution Property
4. $m\overarc{IJ} = m\overarc{KL}$	4. Subtraction Property
5. $m\angle IKJ = m\angle LJK$	5. Inscribed angles that intersect congruent arcs are congruent.

Problem Set 87

1. True
2. False
3. B
4. D
5. D
6. $m\overarc{ADC} = 235$
7. $m\angle KLR = 40$
8. $m\overarc{PL} = 30$
9. $\ell\overarc{SR} = 47.57$
10. $\ell\overarc{KML} = 135.02$
11. $20\sqrt{3}$
12. $DG = 22$
13. $\overline{KN}$ or $\overline{NK}$
14. 39
15. C
16. E
17. $x = 57.5$
18. $y = 130$
19. $x = 30$
20. $x = 73$
21. 66, 18
22. $m\angle H = 103$; $JG = 48$

23.

Statements	Reasons
1. $m\overarc{ABC} = m\overarc{DCB}$	1. Given
2. $m\overarc{AB} + m\overarc{BC} = m\overarc{ABC}$ and $m\overarc{DC} + m\overarc{CB} = m\overarc{DCB}$	2. Arc Addition Postulate
3. $m\overarc{AB} + m\overarc{BC} = m\overarc{DC} + m\overarc{CB}$	3. Substitution Property
4. $m\overarc{AB} = m\overarc{DC}$	4. Subtraction Property
5. $m\angle ACB = m\angle DBC$	5. Inscribed angles that intersect congruent arcs are congruent.

24. **(2)** If a radius is drawn to the point of tangency of a tangent line, then the radius is perpendicular to the tangent line.
    (7) Arc Addition Postulate
    (9) Multiplication Property
    (10) An inscribed angle is equal in measure to one-half the measure of its intercepted arc.
    (11) Substitution Property
    (12) Subtraction Property
    (13) Betweenness of Rays
    (14) Subtraction Property
    (15) Substitution Property

Practice 88

a. 4
b. $m\angle QPR = 66$
c. $x = 137.5$
d. $z = 90$
e.

Statements	Reasons
1. $\overline{QS} \perp \overline{PR}$ in $\odot O$	1. Given
2. $\overline{PS} \cong \overline{RS}$	2. If a line through the center of a circle is perpendicular to a chord, it also bisects the chord.
3. $\overline{OS} \cong \overline{OS}$	3. Reflexive Property
4. $\overline{OP} \cong \overline{OR}$	4. All radii of the same circle are congruent.
5. $\triangle PSO \cong \triangle RSO$	5. Side-Side-Side
6. $\angle POS \cong \angle ROS$	6. C.P.C.T.C.
7. $\angle POQ$ is supplementary to $\angle POS$ and $\angle ROQ$ is supplementary to $\angle ROS$.	7. If two angles are a linear pair, then they are supplementary.
8. $\angle POQ \cong \angle ROQ$	8. Angles supplementary to congruent angles are congruent.
9. $m\angle POQ = m\widehat{PQ}$ and $m\angle ROQ = m\widehat{RQ}$	9. The degree measure of a minor arc is the measure of its central angle.
10. $m\widehat{RQ} = m\widehat{PQ}$	10. Substitution Property

Problem Set 88

1. True
2. True
3. A
4. B
5. D
6. $m\widehat{JK} = 152$
7. $m\angle JLK = 76$
8. $18:19$
9. $21:11$
10. $m\angle U = 106$
11. $\sqrt{6}$
12. $m\angle APB = 65$
13. $m\angle JPH = 48$
14. perimeter = 43
15. perimeter = 68
16. E
17. A
18. $d = 63$
19. $s = 80$
20. $x = 140$
21. $z = 80$
22. 5.41 feet
23. 0.39 miles
24.

Statements	Reasons
1. $m\widehat{AE} + m\widehat{DC} = 180$	1. Given
2. $m\angle ABE = \frac{1}{2}(m\widehat{AE} + m\widehat{DC})$	2. The measure of an angle formed by two chords intersecting in the interior of a circle is equal to one-half the sum of the measures of the two intercepted arcs.
3. $m\angle ABE = \frac{1}{2}(180) = 90$	3. Substitution Property
4. $\angle ABE$ is a right angle.	4. Definition of a right angle
5. $\overline{AC} \perp \overline{DE}$	5. Perpendicular lines intersect to form right angles.

25.

Statements	Reasons
1. $\overline{BE} \perp \overline{AC}$ in $\odot O$	1. Given
2. $\overline{AE} \cong \overline{CE}$	2. If a line through the center of a circle is perpendicular to a

		chord, it also bisects the chord.
3.	$\overline{EO} \cong \overline{EO}$	3. Reflexive Property
4.	$\overline{OA} \cong \overline{OC}$	4. All radii of the same circle are congruent.
5.	$\triangle AEO \cong \triangle CEO$	5. Side-Side-Side
6.	$\angle AOE \cong \angle COE$	6. C.P.C.T.C.
7.	$\angle AOB$ is supplementary to $\angle AOE$ and $\angle COB$ is supplementary to $\angle COE$.	7. If two angles are a linear pair, then they are supplementary.
8.	$\angle AOB \cong \angle COB$	8. Angles supplementary to congruent angles are congruent.
9.	$m\angle AOB = m\overarc{AB}$ and $m\angle COB = m\overarc{CB}$	9. The degree measure of a minor arc is the measure of its central angle.
10.	$m\overarc{CB} = m\overarc{AB}$	10. Substitution Property

Practice 89

a. $m\overarc{SQ} = 60$

b. $\ell\overarc{ABC} = 90\pi$

c. $b = 130$

d. $DE = 6$

e. Statements / Reasons

1.	$m\overarc{MI} = 2m\overarc{LJ}$	1. Given
2.	$m\angle MKI = \frac{1}{2}(m\overarc{MI} - m\overarc{LJ})$	2. The measure of an angle formed by two secants intersecting in the exterior of a circle is equal to one-half the difference of the measures of the two intercepted arcs.
3.	$m\angle MKI = \frac{1}{2}(2m\overarc{LJ} - m\overarc{LJ})$ or $m\angle MKI = \frac{1}{2}(m\overarc{LJ})$	3. Substitution Property
4.	$m\angle KMJ = \frac{1}{2}m\overarc{LJ}$	4. An inscribed angle is equal in measure to one-

		half the measure of its intercepted arc.
5.	$m\angle MKI = m\angle KMJ$	5. Transitive Property
6.	$KJ = MJ$	6. Converse of the Base Angles Theorem
7.	$\triangle MJK$ is isosceles.	7. Definition of an isosceles triangle

Problem Set 89

1. False
2. False
3. C
4. D
5. B
6. $m\overarc{KL} = 115$
7. $m\angle JOL = 160$
8. $m\overarc{BD} = 52$
9. 8π meters
10. $\ell\overarc{RVT} = 128\pi$
11. $XY = 26$
12. $\sqrt{2}$
13. $EG = 27$
14. $AC = 3$
15. $AB = 9$
16. $AC = 12$
17. $h = 10$
18. $b = 132.5$
19. $x = 3$
20. $k = 59$
21. 63 chocolate bunnies
22. 114 turnip trucks
23. Statements / Reasons

1.	$\overline{AC}$ and $\overline{AE}$ are secant segments.	1. Given
2.	$AC \times AB = AE \times AD$	2. If two secant segments are drawn to a circle from the same exterior point, then the product of the lengths of one secant segment and its external segment is equal to the product of the lengths of the other secant segment and its external segment.
3.	$AC = AE$	3. Given

66

4. $AE \times AB = AE \times AD$	4. Substitution Property
5. $\quad AB = AD$	5. Division Property

24.

Statements	Reasons
1. $\quad m\widehat{PT} = 2m\widehat{QS}$	1. Given
2. $m\angle PRT = \frac{1}{2}(m\widehat{PT} - m\widehat{QS})$	2. The measure of an angle formed by two secants intersecting in the exterior of a circle is equal to one-half the difference of the measures of the two intercepted arcs.
3. $m\angle PRT = \frac{1}{2}(2m\widehat{QS} - m\widehat{QS})$ or $m\angle PRT = \frac{1}{2}(m\widehat{QS})$	3. Substitution Property
4. $\quad m\angle RPS = \frac{1}{2}m\widehat{QS}$	4. An inscribed angle is equal in measure to one-half the measure of its intercepted arc.
5. $\quad m\angle PRT = m\angle RPS$	5. Transitive Property
6. $\quad RS = PS$	6. Converse of the Base Angles Theorem
7. $\quad \Delta RSP$ is isosceles.	7. Definition of an isosceles triangle

CHAPTER 13

Practice 90

a. area = 48 ft.^{2}
b. $\angle C$
c. 18.9 in.
d. $x = 70$
e.

Statements	Reasons
1. $\quad m\widehat{EF} = m\widehat{GH}$	1. Given
2. $\quad \overline{EF} \cong \overline{GH}$	2. If two minor arcs of the same circle are congruent, then their intersecting chords are congruent.
3. $\overline{OE} \cong \overline{OH}$ and $\overline{OF} \cong \overline{OG}$	3. All radii of the same circle are congruent.
4. $\Delta EOF \cong \Delta HOG$	4. Side-Side-Side
5. $m\angle EFO = m\angle HGO$	5. C.P.C.T.C.
6. ΔFGO is isosceles.	6. Definition of an isosceles triangle
7. $m\angle OFG = m\angle OGF$	7. Base Angles Theorem
8. $m\angle EFO + m\angle OFG = m\angle HGO + m\angle OGF$	8. Addition Property
9. $m\angle EFO + m\angle OFG = m\angle EFG$ and $m\angle HGO + m\angle OGF = m\angle FGH$	9. Betweenness of Rays
10. $m\angle EFG = m\angle FGH$	10. Substitution Property

Problem Set 90

1. False
2. False
3. D
4. A
5. E
6. $m\angle QRN = 32.5$
7. $m\widehat{RM} = 40$
8. area = 72 in.^{2}
9. area = 192 ft.^{2}
10. $\overline{JK}$ or $\overline{KJ}$
11. $\angle R$
12. diameter = 26
13. 20.2 in.
14. perimeter = 72
15. B
16. $RT = 3$
17. $RQ = 22$
18. $a = 40$
19. $s = 22.5$
20. $x = 65$
21. 40, 16
22. $FG = 22$, $GH = 33$, $HJ = 44$

23.

Statements	Reasons
1. $JK = JL$, $JL > KL$	1. Given
2. $\quad JK > KL$	2. Substitution Property of Inequality
3. $\quad m\angle L > m\angle J$	3. If Unequal Sides, Then Unequal Angles
4. $m\angle L = \frac{1}{2}m\widehat{JK}$, $m\angle J = \frac{1}{2}m\widehat{KL}$	4. An inscribed angle is equal in measure to one-half the measure of its intercepted arc.
5. $\frac{1}{2}m\widehat{JK} > \frac{1}{2}m\widehat{KL}$	5. Substitution Property of Inequality
6. $m\widehat{JK} > m\widehat{KL}$	6. Multiplication Property of Inequality

24.

Statements	Reasons
1. $m\widehat{IJ} = m\widehat{KL}$	1. Given
2. $\overline{IJ} \cong \overline{KL}$	2. If two minor arcs of the same circle are congruent, then their intersecting chords are congruent.
3. $\overline{OI} \cong \overline{OL}$ and $\overline{OJ} \cong \overline{OK}$	3. All radii of the same circle are congruent.
4. $\Delta IOJ \cong \Delta LOK$	4. Side-Side-Side
5. $m\angle IJO = m\angle LKO$	5. C.P.C.T.C.
6. ΔJKO is isosceles.	6. Definition of an isosceles triangle
7. $m\angle OJK = m\angle OKJ$	7. Base Angles Theorem
8. $m\angle IJO + m\angle OJK = m\angle LKO + m\angle OKJ$	8. Addition Property
9. $m\angle IJO + m\angle OJK = m\angle IJK$ and $m\angle LKO + m\angle OKJ = m\angle JKL$	9. Betweenness of Rays
10. $m\angle IJK = m\angle JKL$	10. Substitution Property

Practice 91

a. area = 18
b. area = 144
c. area = 48
d. $AC = 6\sqrt{10}$

e. Statements	Reasons
1. $\overline{VT}$ is tangent to $\odot P$ at U; $\overline{RT}$ is tangent to $\odot P$ at S; $\overline{VR}$ is tangent to $\odot P$ at W.	1. Given
2. $VU = VW$, $UT = TS$, and $WR = SR$	2. If two tangent segments are drawn to a circle from the same exterior point, then they are congruent (equal).
3. $TS = SR$	3. Given
4. $UT = SR$	4. Transitive Property
5. $UT = WR$	5. Transitive Property
6. $VU + UT = VW + WR$	6. Addition Property
7. $VU + UT = VT$ and $VW + WR = VR$	7. Betweenness of Points
8. $VT = VR$	8. Substitution Property
9. $\triangle VTR$ is isosceles.	9. Definition of an isosceles triangle
10. $\angle T \cong \angle R$	10. Base Angles Theorem

Problem Set 91

1. True
2. True
3. E
4. C
5. B
6. $\ell\widehat{VW} = 46.89$ inches
7. $\ell\widehat{CDE} = 75.10$
8. area $= 30$
9. area $= 9$
10. area $= 72$
11. $m\angle D = 60$, $m\angle E = 30$, $m\angle F = 90$
12. area $= 60$
13. A
14. D
15. $m\angle MNL = 73$
16. $m\angle RPT = 24$
17. $b = 88$
18. $y = 50$
19. $x = 6$
20. $QJ = 8\sqrt{5}$
21. 147.20 ft.
22. 51.58 ft.

23. Statements	Reasons
1. $\overline{DC} \cong \overline{AB}$	1. Given
2. $m\widehat{DC} = m\widehat{AB}$	2. If two chords of the same circle are congruent, then their minor arcs are congruent.
3. $m\widehat{DC} + m\widehat{BC} = m\widehat{AB} + m\widehat{BC}$	3. Addition Property
4. $m\widehat{DC} + m\widehat{BC} = m\widehat{DB}$ and $m\widehat{AB} + m\widehat{BC} = m\widehat{AC}$	4. Arc Addition Postulate
5. $m\widehat{DB} = m\widehat{AC}$	5. Substitution Property
6. $\overline{DB} \cong \overline{AC}$	6. If two minor arcs of the same circle are congruent, then their intersected chords are congruent.

24. Statements	Reasons
1. $\overline{HF}$ is tangent to $\odot O$ at C; $\overline{GF}$ is tangent to $\odot O$ at D; $\overline{HG}$ is tangent to $\odot O$ at E.	1. Given
2. $HC = HE$, $CF = FD$, and $EG = DG$	2. If two tangent segments are drawn to a circle from the same exterior point, then they are congruent (equal).
3. $FD = DG$	3. Given
4. $CF = DG$	4. Transitive Property
5. $CF = EG$	5. Transitive Property
6. $HC + CF = HE + EG$	6. Addition Property
7. $HC + CF = HF$ and $HE + EG = HG$	7. Betweenness of Points
8. $HF = HG$	8. Substitution Property
9. $\triangle HFG$ is isosceles.	9. Definition of an isosceles triangle
10. $\angle F \cong \angle G$	10. Base Angles Theorem

Practice 92

a. area $= 330$
b. area $= 27$

c. $a = 90$
d. $y = 11$

e.

Statements	Reasons
1. $\overline{PR}$ is tangent to $\odot O$ at P; $\overline{QR}$ is tangent to $\odot O$ at Q.	1. Given
2. $\overline{PR} \cong \overline{QR}$	2. If two tangent segments are drawn to a circle from the same exterior point, then they are congruent.
3. $\overline{OP} \cong \overline{OQ}$	3. All radii of the same circle are congruent.
4. $\overline{RO} \cong \overline{RO}$	4. Reflexive Property
5. $\triangle RPO \cong \triangle RQO$	5. Side-Side-Side
6. $\angle PRO \cong \angle QRO$	6. C.P.C.T.C.
7. $\overrightarrow{RS}$ bisects $\angle PRQ$.	7. Definition of an angle bisector

Problem Set 92

1. True
2. True
3. E
4. E
5. C
6. $m\overarc{LN} = 49$
7. $m\angle POL = 131$
8. area $= 190$
9. area $= 145$
10. area $= 108$
11. area $= 120$
12. 26
13. $DF = 156$
14. perimeter $= 42.76$
15. perimeter $= 38.56$
16. $FG = 7$
17. $HJ = 12$
18. $a = 81$
19. $x = 10$
20. $y = 34$
21. 54 nail biters
22. 357 monkeys

23.

Statements	Reasons
1. $\overline{JL}$ is tangent to $\odot P$ at K and to $\odot O$ at L; $\overline{JN}$ is tangent to $\odot P$ at M and to $\odot O$ at N.	1. Given
2. $JL = JN$	2. If two tangent segments are drawn to a circle from the same exterior point, then they are congruent.
3. $JL = JK + KL$ and $JN = JM + MN$	3. Betweenness of Points
4. $JK + KL = JM + MN$	4. Substitution Property
5. $JK = JM$	5. If two tangent segments are drawn to a circle from the same exterior point, then they are congruent. (equal).
6. $JM + KL = JM + MN$	6. Substitution Property
7. $KL = MN$	7. Subtraction Property

24.

Statements	Reasons
1. $\overline{BD}$ is tangent to $\odot O$ at B; $\overline{CD}$ is tangent to $\odot O$ at C.	1. Given
2. $\overline{BD} \cong \overline{CD}$	2. If two tangent segments are drawn to a circle from the same exterior point, then they are congruent.
3. $\overline{OB} \cong \overline{OC}$	3. All radii of the same circle are congruent.
4. $\overline{DO} \cong \overline{DO}$	4. Reflexive Property
5. $\triangle DBO \cong \triangle DCO$	5. Side-Side-Side
6. $\angle BDO \cong \angle CDO$	6. C.P.C.T.C.
7. $\overrightarrow{DE}$ bisects $\angle BDC$.	7. Definition of an angle bisector

Practice 93

a. area $= 24\sqrt{3}$ in.^{2}
b. $m\angle V = 90$, $m\angle T = 40$, $m\angle R = 50$
c. $x = 30$
d. $y = 106$
e. A regular polygon (Given). Inscribe the regular polygon in $\odot O$. Draw radii of the regular polygon. Since the polygon is regular, all the sides are congruent. The sides are chords of the circle, so all the intercepted arcs are also congruent. (If chords of the same circle are congruent, then their intercepted minor arcs are

70

congruent.) Therefore, all the central angles are congruent. (The degree measure of a minor arc is the measure of its central angle.)

Problem Set 93

1. False
2. False
3. A
4. B
5. D
6. area = 612 cm^2
7. area = 240 in.^{2}
8. area = 264 in.^{2}
9. area = 104 ft.^{2}
10. $\overline{MN}$ or $\overline{NM}$
11. $\angle T$
12. C
13. E
14. $m\angle BED = 90$, $m\angle EDB = 45$, $m\angle DBE = 45$
15. $m\angle J = 90$, $m\angle H = 35$, $m\angle G = 55$
16. $m\angle DCF = 39$
17. $m\angle RPQ = 18$
18. $r = 34$
19. $x = 15$
20. $y = 25$
21. 400.57 feet
22. 4.26 feet
23. A regular polygon (Given). Inscribe the regular polygon in $\odot Q$. Draw radii of the regular polygon. Since the polygon is regular, all the sides are congruent. The sides are chords of the circle, so all the intercepted arcs are also congruent. (If chords of the same circle are congruent, then their intercepted minor arcs are congruent.) Therefore, all the central angles are congruent. (The degree measure of a minor arc is the measure of its central angle.)

24.

	Statements		Reasons
1.	$OABC$ is a square inside $\odot O$.	1.	Given
2.	$\overline{OA} \perp \overline{AB}$, $\overline{OC} \perp \overline{BC}$ and $OA = OC$	2.	Definition of a square
3.	$MS = NR$	3.	In the same circle, chords equidistant from the center of the circle are equal.
4.	$m\widehat{MS} = m\widehat{NR}$	4.	If two chords of the same circle are congruent,

	Statements		Reasons
			then their minor arcs are congruent.
5.	$m\widehat{MN} + m\widehat{NS} = m\widehat{MS}$ and $m\widehat{NS} + m\widehat{SR} = m\widehat{NR}$	5.	Arc Addition Postulate
6.	$m\widehat{MN} + m\widehat{NS} = m\widehat{NS} + m\widehat{SR}$	6.	Substitution Property
7.	$m\widehat{MN} = m\widehat{SR}$	7.	Subtraction Property

Practice 94

a. B
b. C
c. $y = 5$
d. area = 486
e.

	Statements		Reasons
1.	$m\angle JLM = m\angle KLI$	1.	Given
2.	$m\angle JLM = m\angle JLI + m\angle ILM$ and $m\angle KLI = m\angle KLJ + m\angle JLI$	2.	Betweenness of Rays
3.	$m\angle JLI + m\angle ILM = m\angle KLJ + m\angle JLI$	3.	Substitution Property
4.	$m\angle ILM = m\angle KLJ$	4.	Subtraction Property
5.	$\overline{JL} \cong \overline{IL}$ and $\overline{KL} \cong \overline{ML}$	5.	Given
6.	$\triangle JKL \cong \triangle ILM$	6.	Side-Angle-Side
7.	$\alpha \triangle JKL = \alpha \triangle ILM$	7.	If two figures are congruent, then they have equal areas.
8.	$\alpha \triangle JKL + \alpha \triangle JLI = \alpha \triangle ILM + \alpha \triangle JLI$	8.	Addition Property
9.	area of polygon $KLIJ = \alpha \triangle JKL + \alpha \triangle JLI$ and area of polygon $MLJI = \alpha \triangle ILM + \alpha \triangle JLI$	9.	Area Addition Postulate
10.	area of polygon $KLIJ =$ area of polygon $MLJI$	10.	Substitution Property

Problem Set 94

1. True
2. True
3. E
4. B
5. B
6. 28π in.
7. $\ell \widehat{BAC} = 48\pi$ cm
8. area = 28π

9. area $= 27\pi$
10. A
11. area $= 42$ cm^2
12. 32 in.^{2}
13. 77 feet
14. perimeter $= 120$
15. B
16. $TS = 9$
17. $QU = 20$
18. $d = 17$
19. $n = 36$
20. $x = 4$
21. area $= 384$
22. area $= 216$

23.

	Statements		Reasons
1.	Q is the midpoint of $\overarc{RQS}$.	1.	Given
2.	$m\overarc{RQ} = m\overarc{QS}$	2.	Definition of the midpoint of an arc
3.	$\angle RPQ \cong \angle TPQ$	3.	Inscribed angles that intercept the same or congruent arcs are congruent.
4.	$\overline{PQ}$ is a diameter of $\odot O$.	4.	Given
5.	$\overarc{QSP}$ is a semicircle.	5.	Definition of a semicircle
6.	$\angle QRP$ is a right angle.	6.	An inscribed angle that intercepts a semicircle is a right angle.
7.	$\overline{TQ}$ is a tangent to $\odot O$ at Q.	7.	Given
8.	$\overline{TQ} \perp \overline{QO}$	8.	If a radius is drawn to the point of tangency of a tangent line, the radius is perpendicular to the tangent line.
9.	$\angle TQP$ is a right angle.	9.	Perpendicular lines are lines which intersect to form right angles.
10.	$\angle QRP \cong \angle TQP$	10.	All right angles are congruent.
11.	$\triangle QPT \sim \triangle RPQ$	11.	Angle-Angle Similarity

24.

	Statements		Reasons
1.	$m\angle SQP = m\angle TQR$	1.	Given
2.	$m\angle SQP = m\angle SQR + m\angle RQP$ and $m\angle TQR = m\angle TQS + m\angle SQR$	2.	Betweenness of Rays
3.	$m\angle SQR + m\angle RQP = m\angle TQS + m\angle SQR$	3.	Substitution Property
4.	$m\angle RQP = m\angle TQS$	4.	Subtraction Property
5.	$\overline{SQ} \cong \overline{RQ}$ and $\overline{TQ} \cong \overline{PQ}$	5.	Given
6.	$\triangle STQ \cong \triangle RPQ$	6.	Side-Angle-Side
7.	$\alpha\triangle STQ = \alpha\triangle RPQ$	7.	If two figures are congruent, then they have equal areas.
8.	$\alpha\triangle STQ + \alpha\triangle SQR = \alpha\triangle RPQ + \alpha\triangle SQR$	8.	Addition Property
9.	area of polygon $TQRS = \alpha\triangle STQ + \alpha\triangle SQR$ and area of polygon $PQSR = \alpha\triangle RPQ + \alpha\triangle SQR$	9.	Area Addition Postulate
10.	area of polygon $TQRS = $ area of polygon $PQSR$	10.	Substitution Property

CHAPTER 14

Practice 95

a. $m\overarc{AB} = 120$
b. area = 288
c. B
d. $y = 40$
e. Statements

Statements	Reasons
1. $\overline{QR}$ is a diameter of $\odot O$.	1. Given
2. $\angle RPQ$ and $\angle RSQ$ are right angles.	2. An inscribed angle that intercepts a semicircle is a right angle.
3. $\overline{PQ} \parallel \overline{AO}$ and $\overline{SQ} \parallel \overline{BO}$	3. Given
4. $\angle RPQ \cong \angle RAO$ and $\angle RSQ \cong \angle RBO$	4. If two parallel lines are cut by a transversal, then their corresponding angles are congruent.
5. $\angle RAO$ and $\angle RBO$ are right angles.	5. Congruent angles have equal measures.
6. $\triangle RAO$ and $\triangle RBO$ are right triangles.	6. Definition of a right triangle
7. $\overline{RA} \cong \overline{RB}$	7. Given
8. $\overline{RO} \cong \overline{RO}$	8. Reflexive Property
9. $\triangle RAO \cong \triangle RBO$	9. Hypotenuse-Leg
10. $\overline{AO} \cong \overline{BO}$	10. C.P.C.T.C.
11. $\overline{RP} \cong \overline{RS}$	11. In the same circle, chords equidistant from the center of the circle are congruent.

Problem Set 95

1. True
2. True
3. C
4. D
5. C
6. $m\overarc{JI} = 120$
7. $m\overarc{HIJ} = 300$
8. area = 78
9. D
10. area = 10π ft.^{2}
11. A
12. $DE = 8\sqrt{3}$

13. area = 240 ft.^{2}
14. Surface Area = 104 in.^{2} ; Vol. = 60 in.^{3}
15. Surface Area = 426 cm^2 ; Vol. = 540 cm^3
16. $m\angle F = 36$, $m\angle C = 48$, $m\angle D = 96$
17. $m\angle P = 108$, $m\angle R = 36$, $m\angle T = 36$
18. $x = 15$
19. B
20. $x = 20$
21. 828 munchers
22. 180 foot stompers
23. Statements

Statements	Reasons
1. $\overline{AB}$ and $\overline{CB}$ are tangent segments to $\odot O$.	1. Given
2. $\overline{AB} \perp \overline{AO}$ and $\overline{CB} \perp \overline{CO}$	2. If a radius is drawn to the point of tangency of a tangent line, the radius is perpendicular to the tangent line.
3. $\angle OAB$ and $\angle OCB$ are right angles.	3. Perpendicular lines intersect to form right angles.
4. $m\angle OAB = 90$ and $m\angle OCB = 90$	4. Definition of a right angle
5. $m\angle O + m\angle OAB + m\angle OCB + m\angle B = 360$	5. The sum of the measures of the angles of a quadrilateral is 360.
6. $m\overarc{AC} = m\angle O$	6. The degree measure of a minor arc is the measure of its central angle.
7. $m\overarc{AC} + 90 + 90 + m\angle B = 360$	7. Substitution Property
8. $m\angle B = 180 - m\overarc{AC}$	8. Subtraction Property

24. Statements

Statements	Reasons
1. $\overline{FG}$ is a diameter of $\odot O$.	1. Given
2. $\angle GEF$ and $\angle GHF$ are right angles.	2. An inscribed angle that intercepts a semicircle is a right angle.
3. $\overline{EF} \parallel \overline{JO}$ and $\overline{HF} \parallel \overline{KO}$	3. Given
4. $\angle GEF \cong \angle GJO$ and $\angle GHF \cong \angle GKO$	4. If two parallel lines are cut by a transversal, then their corresponding angles are congruent.

5. ∠GJO and ∠GKO are right angles.

6. ∆GJO and ∆GKO are right triangles.

7. $\overline{GJ} \cong \overline{GK}$

8. $\overline{GO} \cong \overline{GO}$

9. ∆GJO ≅ ∆GKO

10. $\overline{JO} \cong \overline{KO}$

11. $\overline{GE} \cong \overline{GH}$

5. Congruent angles have equal measures.

6. Definition of a right triangle

7. Given

8. Reflexive Property

9. Hypotenuse-Leg

10. C.P.C.T.C.

11. In the same circle, chords equidistant from the center of the circle are congruent.

10. ∆DEB ~ ∆BCE

11. $\dfrac{DB}{BE} = \dfrac{BE}{EC}$

10. Angle-Angle Similarity

11. Converse of the definition of similar triangles

Problem Set 96

1. True
2. False
3. B
4. E
5. D
6. area = 88 in.^{2}
7. area = 27π
8. area = 48π in.^{2}
9. C
10. D
11. A
12. total area = 304
13. total area = 195
14. volume = 105
15. volume 1,778
16. B
17. perimeter = 12π
18. $m = 51$
19. $x = 32$
20. E
21. A
22. D

Practice 96

a. area = 22.5π in.^{2}
b. area = 780
c. volume = 1,500
d. A
e.

Statements	Reasons
1. $\overline{EC}$ is a diameter of ⊙O.	1. Given
2. ∠EBC is a right angle.	2. An inscribed angle that intercepts a semicircle is a right angle.
3. $\overline{DE} \perp \overline{DB}$	3. Given
4. ∠BDE is a right angle.	4. Perpendicular lines intersect to form right angles.
5. ∠EBC ≅ ∠BDE	5. All right angles are congruent.
6. $\overline{DE}$ is tangent to ⊙O at E.	6. Given
7. $m\angle DEB = \dfrac{1}{2}m\overset{\frown}{EB}$	7. The measure of an angle formed by a tangent and a chord drawn to the point of tangency is equal to one-half the measure of the intercepted arc.
8. $m\angle BCE = \dfrac{1}{2}m\overset{\frown}{EB}$	8. An inscribed angle is equal in measure to one-half the measure of its intercepted arc.
9. $m\angle DEB = m\angle BCE$	9. Transitive Property

23.

Statements	Reasons
1. $\overset{\frown}{AB} \cong \overset{\frown}{CD}$	1. Given
2. $\overline{AB} \cong \overline{CD}$	2. If two minor arcs of the same circle are congruent, then their intersecting chords are congruent.
3. $\overline{BC} \parallel \overline{AD}$	3. Given
4. ABCD is an isosceles trapezoid.	4. Definition of an isosceles trapezoid
5. ∠A ≅ ∠D	5. Base angles of an isosceles trapezoid are congruent.

24.

Statements	Reasons
1. $\overline{LN}$ is a diameter of ⊙O.	1. Given
2. ∠LMN is a right angle.	2. An inscribed angle that intercepts a semicircle is a right angle.

3.	$\overline{KL} \perp \overline{KM}$	3. Given	
4.	$\angle MKL$ is a right angle.	4. Perpendicular lines intersect to form right angles.	

5.	$\angle LMN \cong \angle MKL$	5. All right angles are congruent.	
6.	$\overline{KL}$ is tangent to $\odot O$ at L.	6. Given	
7.	$m\angle KLM = \frac{1}{2} m\widehat{LM}$	7. The measure of an angle formed by a tangent and a chord drawn to the point of tangency is equal to one-half the measure of the intercepted arc.	
8.	$m\angle MNL = \frac{1}{2} m\widehat{LM}$	8. An inscribed angle is equal in measure to one-half the measure of its intercepted arc.	
9.	$m\angle KLM = m\angle MNL$	9. Transitive Property	
10.	$\triangle KLM \sim \triangle MNL$	10. Angle-Angle Similarity	
11.	$\frac{KM}{ML} = \frac{ML}{LN}$	11. Converse of the definition of similar triangles	

Practice 97

a. area = 30
b. total area = 40
c. volume = 150
d. D
e. Statements

Statements	Reasons
1. UVWXYZ is a regular polygon with center O.	1. Given
2. Draw $\overline{OU}$ and $\overline{OW}$.	2. Two points determine a line.
3. $\overline{UV} \cong \overline{WV}$	3. Definition of a regular polygon
4. $\overline{OU} \cong \overline{OW}$	4. Definition of the radius of a regular polygon
5. $\overline{OV} \cong \overline{OV}$	5. Reflexive Property
6. $\triangle UVO \cong \triangle WVO$	6. Side-Side-Side
7. $\angle UVO \cong \angle WVO$	7. C.P.C.T.C.
8. $\overline{OV}$ bisects $\angle UVW$.	8. Definition of an angle bisector

Problem Set 97

1. True
2. True
3. A
4. C
5. B
6. E
7. E
8. area = 348
9. area = 7.5
10. D
11. E
12. C
13. total area = 62
14. total area = 133
15. volume = 846
16. volume = 324
17. volume = 63
18. $a = 4$
19. $b = 72$
20. A
21. $DO = 9$
22. $AK = 24$
23. Statements

Statements	Reasons
1. $\overline{FG} \parallel \overline{DE}$	1. Given
2. Draw $\overline{DG}$.	2. Two points determine a line.
3. $m\angle FGD = m\angle EDG$	3. If two parallel lines are cut by a transversal, then their alternate interior angles are equal.
4. $m\angle FGD = \frac{1}{2} m\widehat{DF}$ and $m\angle EDG = \frac{1}{2} m\widehat{EG}$	4. An inscribed angle is equal in measure to one-half the measure of its intercepted arc.
5. $\frac{1}{2} m\widehat{DF} = \frac{1}{2} m\widehat{EG}$	5. Substitution Property
6. $m\widehat{DF} = m\widehat{EG}$	6. Multiplication Property
7. $\widehat{DF} \cong \widehat{EG}$	7. Arcs with equal measures are congruent.

24. Statements

Statements	Reasons
1. ABCDEFGH is a regular polygon with center O.	1. Given
2. Draw $\overline{OA}$ and $\overline{OC}$.	2. Two points determine a line.

	Statements		Reasons
3.	$\overline{AB} \cong \overline{CB}$	3.	Definition of a regular polygon
4.	$\overline{OA} \cong \overline{OC}$	4.	Definition of the radius of a regular polygon
5.	$\overline{OB} \cong \overline{OB}$	5.	Reflexive Property
6.	$\triangle ABO \cong \triangle CBO$	6.	Side-Side-Side
7.	$\angle ABO \cong \angle CBO$	7.	C.P.C.T.C.
8.	$\overline{OB}$ bisects $\angle ABC$.	8.	Definition of an angle bisector

Practice 98

a. area = 45
b. total area = 352
c. volume = 36π
d. $\ell \overset{\frown}{CED} = 20$
e. Statements

	Statements		Reasons
1.	$\overline{OP}$ is an apothem of regular polygon $QRSTUVWX$.	1.	Given
2.	$\overline{OP} \perp \overline{XW}$	2.	Definition of an apothem of a regular polygon
3.	$\angle XPO$ and $\angle WPO$ are right angles.	3.	Perpendicular lines intersect to form right angles.
4.	$\triangle XPO$ and $\triangle WPO$ are right triangles.	4.	Definition of a right triangle
5.	$\overline{OX} \cong \overline{OW}$	5.	Definition of the radius of a regular polygon
6.	$\overline{OP} \cong \overline{OP}$	6.	Reflexive Property
7.	$\triangle XPO \cong \triangle WPO$	7.	Hypotenuse-Leg
8.	$\angle XOP \cong \angle WOP$	8.	C.P.C.T.C.
9.	$\overline{OP}$ bisects $\angle XOW$.	9.	Definition of an angle bisector

Problem Set 98

1. True
2. True
3. C
4. D
5. A
6. area = 40
7. area = 32
8. B
9. total area = 375
10. total area = 184

11. volume = 42 in.^{3}
12. volume = $1,472\pi$
13. volume = 180π
14. perimeter = 64
15. perimeter = 80
16. $m\angle BPD = 115$
17. $m\angle JPH = 43$
18. $a = 8$
19. $c = 72$
20. $\ell \overset{\frown}{IKJ} = 10$
21. 3.58 feet
22. 14.91 feet

23.

	Statements		Reasons
1.	$\overline{BC}$ is tangent to $\odot O$ at B.	1.	Given
2.	$\angle ABC$ is a right angle.	2.	If a radius is drawn to the point of tangency, the radius is perpendicular to the tangent line.
3.	$\overline{AB}$ is a diameter of $\odot O$.	3.	Given
4.	$\angle ADB$ is a right angle.	4.	An inscribed angle that intercepts a semicircle is a right angle.
5.	$\overline{BD}$ is an altitude of right $\triangle ABC$.	5.	Definition of an altitude
6.	$\triangle ABC \sim \triangle ADB \sim \triangle BDC$	6.	The altitude to the hypotenuse of a right triangle forms two triangles similar to each other and to the original triangle.

24.

	Statements		Reasons
1.	$\overline{OP}$ is an apothem of regular polygon $ABCDEF$.	1.	Given
2.	$\overline{OP} \perp \overline{BC}$	2.	Definition of an apothem of a regular polygon
3.	$\angle BPO$ and $\angle CPO$ are right angles.	3.	Perpendicular lines intersect to form right angles.
4.	$\triangle BPO$ and $\triangle CPO$ are right triangles.	4.	Definition of a right triangle
5.	$\overline{OB} \cong \overline{OC}$	5.	Definition of the radius of a regular polygon
6.	$\overline{OP} \cong \overline{OP}$	6.	Reflexive Property

7.	$\triangle BPO \cong \triangle CPO$	7.	Hypotenuse-Leg
8.	$\angle BOP \cong \angle COP$	8.	C.P.C.T.C.
9.	$\overline{OP}$ bisects $\angle BOC$.	9.	Definition of an angle bisector

Practice 99

a. D
b. total area = 944
c. 41.52 m^3
d. $x = 12$
e.

	Statements		Reasons
1.	Quadriiateral *FGHJ* is inscribed in $\odot O$.	1.	Given
2.	$m\angle F = \frac{1}{2}m\widehat{GHJ}$ and $m\angle H = \frac{1}{2}m\widehat{JFG}$	2.	An inscribed angle is equal in measure to one-half the measure of its intercepted arc.
3.	$m\angle F + m\angle H = \frac{1}{2}m\widehat{GHJ} + \frac{1}{2}m\widehat{JFG}$	3.	Addition Property
4.	$m\widehat{GHJ} + m\widehat{JFG} = 360$	4.	Arc Addition Postulate
5.	$\frac{1}{2}m\widehat{GHJ} + \frac{1}{2}m\widehat{JFG} = 180$	5.	Multiplication Property
6.	$m\angle F + m\angle H = 180$	6.	Substitution Property
7.	$m\angle F + m\angle G + m\angle H + m\angle J = 360$	7.	The sum of the measures of the angles of a quad-rilateral is 360.
8.	$180 + m\angle G + m\angle J = 360$	8.	Substitution Property
9.	$m\angle G + m\angle J = 180$	9.	Subtraction Property

Problem Set 99

1. True
2. True
3. B
4. A
5. D
6. $m\widehat{AB} = 100$
7. $m\angle BDC = 55$
8. C
9. area = 64
10. A

11. surface area = 100π
12. total area = 2,592
13. volume = 64
14. volume = 288π
15. volume = 5.22 m^3
16. $KM = 3$
17. $IJ = 11$
18. $b - d = 90$
19. $n = 40$
20. $x = 15$
21. 2,170 apples
22. 9,090 grapes
23.

	Statements		Reasons
1.	$\overleftrightarrow{AB}$ is tangent to $\odot O$ at *A* and $\overleftrightarrow{CD}$ is tangent to $\odot O$ at *D*.	1.	Given
2.	$\overline{CA} \cong \overline{CD}$	2.	If two tangent segments are drawn to a circle from the same exterior point, then they are congruent.
3.	$\overleftrightarrow{AB}$ is tangent to $\odot P$ at *B* and $\overleftrightarrow{CD}$ is tangent to $\odot P$ at *D*.	3.	Given
4.	$\overline{CD} \cong \overline{CB}$	4.	If two tangent segments are drawn to a circle from the same exterior point, then they are congruent.
5.	$\overline{CA} \cong \overline{CB}$	5.	Transitive Property
6.	$\overline{CD}$ bisects $\overline{AB}$.	6.	Definition of a segment bisector

24.

	Statements		Reasons
1.	Quadrilateral *ABCD* is inscribed in $\odot O$.	1.	Given
2.	$m\angle A = \frac{1}{2}m\widehat{BCD}$ and $m\angle C = \frac{1}{2}m\widehat{DAB}$	2.	An inscribed angle is equal in measure to one-half the measure of its intercepted arc.
3.	$m\angle A + m\angle C = \frac{1}{2}m\widehat{BCD} + \frac{1}{2}m\widehat{DAB}$	3.	Addition Property
4.	$m\widehat{BCD} + m\widehat{DAB} = 360$	4.	Arc Addition Postulate

5. $\frac{1}{2}m\widehat{BCD} + \frac{1}{2}m\widehat{DAB} = 180$ 5. Multiplication Property

6. $m\angle A + m\angle C = 180$ 6. Substitution Property

7. $m\angle A + m\angle B + m\angle C + m\angle D = 360$ 7. The sum of the measures of the angles of a quadrilateral is 360.

8. $180 + m\angle B + m\angle D = 360$ 8. Substitution Property

9. $m\angle B + m\angle D = 180$ 9. Subtraction Property

Practice 100

a. E
b. total area = 448
c. 1 : 64
d. 5
e.

Statements	Reasons
1. $\square EFHG$ is inscribed in $\odot O$ of radius r.	1. Given
2. Draw diagonals $\overline{EH}$ and $\overline{FG}$ of $\square EFHG$.	2. Two points determine a unique straight line.
3. $\alpha\square EFHG = \frac{1}{2}(EH \times FG)$	3. The area of a square (rhombus) is equal to one-half the product of the lengths of the two diagonals.
4. $\angle GEF$ and $\angle HFE$ are right angles.	4. Definition of a square
5. $m\angle GEF = 90$ and $m\angle HFE = 90$	5. Definition of a right angle
6. $m\widehat{GHF} = 180$ and $m\widehat{EGH} = 180$	6. An inscribed angle is equal in measure to one-half the measure of its intercepted arc.
7. $\widehat{GHF}$ and $\widehat{EGH}$ are semicircles.	7. Definition of a semicircle
8. $\overline{EH}$ and $\overline{FG}$ are diameters of $\odot O$.	8. Definition of a diameter
9. $EH = 2r$ and $FG = 2r$	9. The length of the diameter of a circle is twice the length of the radius.

10. $\alpha\square EFHG = \frac{1}{2}(2r \times 2r)$ 10. Substitution Property

11. $\alpha\square EFHG = 2r^2$ 11. Multiplication

Problem Set 100

1. False
2. False
3. D
4. A
5. C
6. A
7. B
8. total area = 112
9. total area = 360
10. volume = $1,200\pi$
11. volume = $1,344$ in.^{3}
12. volume = 144π
13. $125 : 1$
14. $4 : 9$
15. $27 : 1$
16. E
17. D
18. $m\angle QPS = 44$
19. $m\angle JKL = 22$
20. $CD = 8$
21. $s = 17$
22. $r = 8$
23.

Statements	Reasons
1. From point M, draw the altitude intersecting $\overline{PQ}$ at point I.	1. Two points determine a unique straight line.
2. $\alpha\triangle PNM = \frac{1}{2}(PN)(MI)$ and $\alpha\triangle QNM = \frac{1}{2}(QN)(MI)$	2. The area of a triangle is equal to one-half the product of the base and the altitude.
3. N is the midpoint of $\overline{PQ}$.	3. Given
4. $QN = PN$	4. Definition of a midpoint
5. $\alpha\triangle PNM = \frac{1}{2}(QN)(MI)$	5. Substitution Property
6. $\alpha\triangle PNM = \alpha\triangle QNM$	6. Transitive Property

24.

Statements	Reasons
1. $\square MNQP$ is inscribed in $\odot O$ of radius r.	1. Given
2. Draw diagonals $\overline{MQ}$ and $\overline{NP}$ of $\square MNQP$.	2. Two points determine a unique straight line.

3. $\alpha\square MNQP = \frac{1}{2}(MQ \times NP)$

3. The area of a square (rhombus) is equal to one-half the product of the lengths of the two diagonals.

4. $\angle PMN$ and $\angle QNM$ are right angles.

4. Definition of a square

5. $m\angle PMN = 90$ and $m\angle QNM = 90$

5. Definition of a right angle

6. $m\overset{\frown}{PQN} = 180$ and $m\overset{\frown}{MPQ} = 180$

6. An inscribed angle is equal in measure to one-half the measure of its intercepted arc.

7. $\overset{\frown}{PQN}$ and $\overset{\frown}{MPQ}$ are semicircles of $\odot O$.

7. Definition of a semicircle

8. $\overline{MQ}$ and $\overline{NP}$ are diameters of $\odot O$.

8. Definition of a diameter

9. $MQ = 2r$ and $NP = 2r$

9. The length of the diameter of a circle is twice the length of the radius.

10. $\alpha\square MNQP = \frac{1}{2}(2r \times 2r)$

10. Substitution Property

11. $\alpha\square MNQP = 2r^2$

11. Multiplication

CHAPTER 15

Practice 101

a. $J(0,3)$, $L(4,0)$

b. C

c. $27:125$

d. $r = 8$

e.

Statements	Reasons
1. $\triangle PST \cong \triangle QRT$ and $\triangle PQT \cong \triangle SRT$	1. Given
2. $\overline{PS} \cong \overline{QR}$ and $\overline{PQ} \cong \overline{SR}$	2. C.P.C.T.C.
3. $PQRS$ is a parallelogram.	3. If both pairs of opposite sides are congruent, then a quadrilateral is a parallelogram.
4. $\overline{PS} \parallel \overline{QR}$ and $\overline{PQ} \parallel \overline{SR}$	4. Definition of a parallelogram

Problem Set 101

1. True
2. True
3. A
4. D
5. D
6. $A(0,4)$, $C(5,0)$
7. $B(-3,2)$, $D(2,-1)$
8. $Q(6,3)$
9. $m\widehat{PJ} = 102$
10. $m\angle JNK = 53$
11. area $= 12\pi$
12. B
13. $4:9$
14. $125:343$
15. volume $= 768$
16. volume $= 220$
17. D
18. $r = 2$
19. $r = 1$
20. $r = 10$
21. 11.79 feet
22. 30.94 in.

23.

Statements	Reasons
1. $\widehat{MQN}$ is a semicircle of $\odot O$.	1. Given
2. $\angle P$ and $\angle Q$ are right angles.	2. An inscribed angle that intercepts a semicircle is a right angle.
3. $\triangle MNP$ and $\triangle NMQ$ are right triangles.	3. Definition of a right triangle
4. $\overline{MN} \cong \overline{MN}$	4. Reflexive Property
5. $\overline{MP} \cong \overline{NQ}$	5. Given
6. $\overline{MP} \cong \overline{NQ}$	6. If two minor arcs of the same circle are congruent, then their intersecting chords are congruent.
7. $\triangle MNP \cong \triangle NMQ$	7. Hypotenuse-Leg

24.

Statements	Reasons
1. $\triangle ADE \cong \triangle BCE$ and $\triangle ABE \cong \triangle DCE$	1. Given
2. $\overline{AD} \cong \overline{BC}$ and $\overline{AB} \cong \overline{DC}$	2. C.P.C.T.C.
3. $ABCD$ is a parallelogram.	3. If both pairs of opposite sides are congruent, then a quadrilateral is a parallelogram.
4. $\overline{AD} \parallel \overline{BC}$ and $\overline{AB} \parallel \overline{DC}$	4. Definition of a parallelogram

Practice 102

a. $F(a,0)$, $I(b,0)$

b. $(-1.5, 3.5)$

c. $EH = 6$, $HG = 2\sqrt{2}$

d. area $= 7$

e.

Statements	Reasons
1. $\overline{DF} \parallel \overline{VG}$	1. Given
2. Draw chord $\overline{DG}$.	2. Two points determine a unique straight line.
3. $m\angle FDG = m\angle DGV$	3. If two parallel lines are cut by a transversal, then their alternate interior angles are equal.
4. $\frac{1}{2}m\widehat{FG} = m\angle FDG$ and $\frac{1}{2}m\widehat{DV} = m\angle DGV$	4. An inscribed angle is equal in measure to one-half the measure of its intercepted arc.
5. $\frac{1}{2}m\widehat{FG} = \frac{1}{2}m\widehat{DV}$	5. Substitution Property
6. $m\widehat{FG} = m\widehat{DV}$	6. Multiplication Property

	Statements	Reasons
7.	$m\overset{\frown}{FG} + m\overset{\frown}{VG} = m\overset{\frown}{DV} + m\overset{\frown}{VG}$	7. Addition Property
8.	$m\overset{\frown}{FGV} = m\overset{\frown}{FG} + m\overset{\frown}{VG}$ and $m\overset{\frown}{DVG} = m\overset{\frown}{DV} + m\overset{\frown}{VG}$	8. Arc Addition Postulate
9.	$m\overset{\frown}{FGV} = m\overset{\frown}{DVG}$	9. Substitution Property
10.	$\angle KDF \cong \angle KFD$	10. Inscribed angles that intercept congruent arcs are congruent.
11.	$\overline{FK} \cong \overline{DK}$	11. Converse of the Base Angles Theorem

Problem Set 102

1. True
2. True
3. D
4. B
5. A
6. $V(a,a)$, $W(a,0)$
7. $M(0,c)$, $P(a,0)$
8. $(-1,3)$
9. $(\frac{1}{2}, -4)$
10. $AC = 5$
11. $JK = 6$, $KL = 5$
12. $RS = 5$, $ST = \sqrt{10}$
13. area $= 7.5$
14. C
15. E
16. perimeter $= 30$
17. total area $= 358$ in.^{2}
18. A
19. total area $= 392$ cm^2
20. $x = 6$
21. $m\overset{\frown}{BC} + m\overset{\frown}{AD} = 240$
22. $h = 20$

23.

	Statements	Reasons
1.	$\overline{HM} \parallel \overline{IN}$, $\overline{HM} \parallel \overline{GJ}$, $\overline{GJ} \parallel \overline{IN}$, $\overline{HI} \parallel \overline{MN}$, $\overline{HG} \parallel \overline{MJ}$, $\overline{GI} \parallel \overline{JN}$	1. Given
2.	$HGJM$, $GINJ$ and $HINM$ are parallelograms.	2. Definition of a parallelogram
3.	$\overline{HG} \cong \overline{MJ}$, $\overline{GI} \cong \overline{JN}$, $\overline{HI} \cong \overline{MN}$	3. If a quadrilateral is a parallelogram, then both pairs of opposite sides are congruent.

4.	$\triangle HGI \cong \triangle MJN$	4. Side-Side-Side

24.

	Statements	Reasons
1.	$\overline{TR} \parallel \overline{US}$	1. Given
2.	Draw chord TS.	2. Two points determine a unique straight line.
3.	$m\angle RTS = m\angle TSU$	3. If two parallel lines are cut by a transversal, then their alternate interior angles are equal.
4.	$m\angle RTS = \frac{1}{2} m\overset{\frown}{RS}$ and $m\angle TSU = \frac{1}{2} m\overset{\frown}{TU}$	4. An inscribed angle is equal in measure to one-half the measure of its intercepted arc.
5.	$\frac{1}{2} m\overset{\frown}{RS} = \frac{1}{2} m\overset{\frown}{TU}$	5. Substitution Property
6.	$m\overset{\frown}{RS} = m\overset{\frown}{TU}$	6. Multiplication Property
7.	$m\overset{\frown}{RS} + m\overset{\frown}{US} = m\overset{\frown}{TU} + m\overset{\frown}{US}$	7. Addition Property
8.	$m\overset{\frown}{RSU} = m\overset{\frown}{RS} + m\overset{\frown}{US}$ and $m\overset{\frown}{TUS} = m\overset{\frown}{TU} + m\overset{\frown}{US}$	8. Arc Addition Postulate
9.	$m\overset{\frown}{RSU} = m\overset{\frown}{TUS}$	9. Substitution Property
10.	$\angle VTR \cong \angle VRT$	10. Inscribed angles that intercept congruent arcs are congruent.
11.	$\overline{RV} \cong \overline{TV}$	11. Converse of the Base Angles Theorem

Practice 103

a. $(-\frac{1}{2}, -\frac{5}{2})$
b. $PQ = c - b$
c. B
d. $r = 7.84$

e.

	Statements	Reasons
1.	$\overline{ZF} \cong \overline{ZG}$	1. Given
2.	$\angle ZFG \cong \angle ZGF$	2. Base Angles Theorem
3.	$m\angle ZGF = \frac{1}{2} m\overset{\frown}{HEF}$ and $m\angle ZFG = \frac{1}{2} m\overset{\frown}{EHG}$	3. An inscribed angle is equal in measure to one-half the measure of its intercepted arc.

	Statements		Reasons
4.	$\frac{1}{2}m\widehat{HEF} = \frac{1}{2}m\widehat{EHG}$	4.	Transitive Property
5.	$m\widehat{HEF} = m\widehat{EHG}$	5.	Multiplication Property
6.	$m\widehat{HE} + m\widehat{EF} = m\widehat{HEF}$ and $m\widehat{EH} + m\widehat{HG} = m\widehat{EHG}$	6.	Arc Addition Postulate
7.	$m\widehat{HE} + m\widehat{EF} = m\widehat{EH} + m\widehat{HG}$	7.	Substitution Property
8.	$m\widehat{EF} = m\widehat{HG}$	8.	Subtraction Property
9.	$\overline{EF} \cong \overline{HG}$	9.	If two minor arcs of the same circle are congruent, then their intersecting chords are congruent.
10.	$\overline{EY} \perp \overline{FG}$ at point Y and $\overline{HX} \perp \overline{FG}$ at point X.	10.	Given
11.	$\angle EYF$ and $\angle HXG$ are right angles.	11.	Perpendicular lines intersect to form right angles.
12.	$\angle EYF \cong \angle HXG$	12.	All right angles are congruent.
13.	$\Delta EFY \cong \Delta HGX$	13.	Angle-Angle-Side
14.	$\overline{EY} \cong \overline{HX}$	14.	C.P.C.T.C.

Problem Set 103

1. False
2. False
3. B
4. E
5. C
6. A
7. B
8. D
9. $(-\frac{1}{2}, -3)$
10. $LK = 4\sqrt{2}$
11. $QP = a - d$
12. slope $= 2$
13. slope $= -3$
14. A
15. C
16. area $= 42\pi$
17. E
18. volume $= 816$ in.^{3}
19. volume $= 200$

20. $x = 36$
21. $h = 2$
22. $r = 5.23$

23.

	Statements		Reasons
1.	$\overline{LN}$ and $\overline{RN}$ are secant segments. $\overline{NT}$ is tangent to both $\odot O$ and $\odot P$ at point T.	1.	Given
2.	$LN \times MN = (NT)^2$ and $RN \times QN = (NT)^2$	2.	If a tangent segment and a secant segment are drawn to a circle from the same exterior point, then the square of the length of the tangent segment is equal to the product of the lengths of the secant segment and its external segment.
3.	$LN \times MN = RN \times QN$	3.	Transitive Property

24.

	Statements		Reasons
1.	$\overline{MQ} \cong \overline{MS}$	1.	Given
2.	$\angle MSQ \cong \angle MQS$	2.	Base Angles Theorem
3.	$m\angle MSQ = \frac{1}{2}m\widehat{QPR}$ and $m\angle MQS = \frac{1}{2}m\widehat{PRS}$	3.	An inscribed angle is equal in measure to one-half the measure of its intercepted arc.
4.	$\frac{1}{2}m\widehat{QPR} = \frac{1}{2}m\widehat{PRS}$	4.	Transitive Property
5.	$m\widehat{QPR} = m\widehat{PRS}$	5.	Multiplication Property
6.	$m\widehat{QP} + m\widehat{PR} = m\widehat{QPR}$ and $m\widehat{PR} + m\widehat{RS} = m\widehat{PRS}$	6.	Arc Addition Postulate
7.	$m\widehat{QP} + m\widehat{PR} = m\widehat{PR} + m\widehat{RS}$	7.	Substitution Property
8.	$m\widehat{QP} = m\widehat{RS}$	8.	Subtraction Property
9.	$\overline{QP} \cong \overline{RS}$	9.	If two minor arcs of the same circle are congruent, then their intersecting chords are congruent.
10.	$\overline{PI} \perp \overline{QS}$ at point I and $\overline{RJ} \perp \overline{QS}$ at point J.	10.	Given

11.	$\angle PIQ$ and $\angle RJS$ are right angles.	11.	Perpendicular lines intersect to form right angles.
12.	$\angle PIQ \cong \angle RJS$	12.	All right angles are congruent.
13.	$\Delta PIQ \cong \Delta RJS$	13.	Angle-Angle-Side
14.	$\overline{PI} \cong \overline{RJ}$	14.	C.P.C.T.C.

Practice 104

a. area $= 12$
b. A
c. C
d. $(4,5)$
e.

	Statements		Reasons
1.	$\overline{KJ}$ is tangent to $\odot O$ at point J.	1.	Given
2.	$m\angle JIM = \frac{1}{2}m\widehat{JN}$	2.	An inscribed angle is equal in measure to one-half the measure of its intercepted arc.
3.	$m\angle KJN = \frac{1}{2}m\widehat{JN}$	3.	The measure of an angle formed by a tangent and a chord drawn to the point of tangency is equal to one-half the measure of the intercepted arc.
4.	$m\angle KJN = m\angle JIM$	4.	Transitive Property
5.	$\angle IJM$ is a right angle.	5.	If a radius is drawn to the point of tangency of a tangent line, then the radius is perpendicular to the tangent line.
6.	$m\angle IJM = 90$	6.	Definition of a right angle
7.	$\overline{IJ} \parallel \overline{LK}$	7.	Given
8.	$\angle IJM$ and $\angle JKL$ are supplementary.	8.	If two parallel lines are cut (crossed) by a transversal, then interior angles on the same side of the transversal are supplementary.
9.	$m\angle IJM + m\angle JKL = 180$	9.	Definition of supplementary

10.	$90 + m\angle JKL = 180$	10.	Substitution Property
11.	$m\angle JKL = 90$	11.	Subtraction Property
12.	$\angle JKL \cong \angle IJM$	12.	Angles with equal measures are congruent.
13.	$\Delta JKL \sim \Delta IJM$	13.	Angle-Angle Similarity
14.	$\dfrac{JL}{IM} = \dfrac{KL}{JM}$	14.	Converse of the definition of similar triangles

Problem Set 104

1. True
2. True
3. E
4. B
5. B
6. $A(0,b)$, $B(a,b)$
7. $G(a,a)$, $H(a,0)$
8. area $= 48$
9. surface area $= 196\pi$
10. area $= 16$
11. $AB = 5$, $BC = 5$
12. D
13. $m\angle QPS = 44$
14. $m\angle JKL = 22$
15. slope $= 0$
16. slope $= \dfrac{1}{2}$
17. E
18. A
19. D
20. $a = 2\sqrt{2}$
21. $r = 4$
22. $(5,5)$
23.

	Statements		Reasons
1.	Draw $\overline{KL}$, the perpendicular segment from K to $\overline{GH}$.	1.	Through a point not on a line, there exists exactly one perpendicular to the given line.
2.	$\overline{GH} \parallel \overline{JK}$	2.	Given
3.	The distance from K to $\overline{GH}$ is KL.	3.	Definition of the distance between a point and a line

4. The distance from J to $\overline{GH}$ is KL.

4. The distance between parallel lines is constant.

5. $\overline{KL}$ is the altitude of both $\triangle GKH$ and $\triangle GJH$.

5. Definition of an altitude

6. $\alpha\triangle GKH = \dfrac{1}{2}GH \times KL$

   and $\alpha\triangle GJH = \dfrac{1}{2}GH \times KL$

6. Area of a triangle

7. $\alpha\triangle GJH = \alpha\triangle GKH$

7. Transitive Property

10. $90 + m\angle QRS = 180$

10. Substitution Property

11. $m\angle QRS = 90$

11. Subtraction Property

12. $\angle QRS \cong \angle PQU$

12. Angles with equal measures are congruent.

13. $\triangle QRS \sim \triangle PQU$

13. Angle-Angle Similarity

14. $\dfrac{QS}{PU} = \dfrac{RS}{QU}$

14. Converse of the definition of similar triangles

24.

Statements	Reasons
1. $\overline{RQ}$ is tangent to $\odot O$ at point Q.	1. Given
2. $m\angle QPU = \dfrac{1}{2}m\widehat{QV}$	2. An inscribed angle is equal in measure to one-half the measure of its intercepted arc.
3. $m\angle RQV = \dfrac{1}{2}m\widehat{QV}$	3. The measure of an angle formed by a tangent and a chord drawn to the point of tangency is equal to one-half the measure of the intercepted arc.
4. $m\angle RQV = m\angle QPU$	4. Transitive Property
5. $\angle PQU$ is a right angle.	5. If a radius is drawn to the point of tangency of a tangent line, then the radius is perpendicular to the tangent line.
6. $m\angle PQU = 90$	6. Definition of a right angle
7. $\overline{PQ} \parallel \overline{SR}$	7. Given
8. $\angle PQU$ and $\angle QRS$ are supplementary.	8. If two parallel lines are cut (crossed) by a transversal, then their interior angles on the same side of the transversal are supplementary.
9. $m\angle PQU + m\angle QRS = 180$	9. Definition of supplementary angles

Practice 105

a. $E(2c, 0)$

b. $\left(\dfrac{b}{2}, \dfrac{c}{2}\right)$

c. D

d. E

e. Right triangle GHI; J is the midpoint of $\overline{GH}$ (Given). Of course, we know that by the Midpoint Formula, the coordinates of point J are $\left(\dfrac{0+a}{2}, \dfrac{0+b}{2}\right)$ or $\left(\dfrac{a}{2}, \dfrac{b}{2}\right)$. Next, by the Distance Formula we can say that $JI = \sqrt{\left(\dfrac{a}{2}-a\right)^2 + \left(\dfrac{b}{2}-0\right)^2} = \sqrt{\left(\dfrac{a}{2}-\dfrac{2a}{2}\right)^2 + \left(\dfrac{b}{2}-0\right)^2}$

$= \sqrt{\left(-\dfrac{a}{2}\right)^2 + \left(\dfrac{b}{2}\right)^2} = \sqrt{\dfrac{a^2}{4}+\dfrac{b^2}{4}} = \sqrt{\dfrac{a^2+b^2}{4}}$

$= \dfrac{\sqrt{a^2+b^2}}{2}$. The Distance Formula can also be

used to show that $JH = \sqrt{\left(a-\dfrac{a}{2}\right)^2 + \left(b-\dfrac{b}{2}\right)^2}$

$= \sqrt{\left(\dfrac{2a}{2}-\dfrac{a}{2}\right)^2 + \left(\dfrac{2b}{2}-\dfrac{b}{2}\right)^2} = \sqrt{\left(\dfrac{a}{2}\right)^2 + \left(\dfrac{b}{2}\right)^2}$

$= \sqrt{\dfrac{a^2}{4}+\dfrac{b^2}{4}} = \sqrt{\dfrac{a^2+b^2}{4}} = \dfrac{\sqrt{a^2+b^2}}{2}$. So, by

the Transitive Property, $JI = JH$.

Problem Set 105

1. True
2. False
3. B
4. A

5. E

6. $S(0,a)$, $T(b,a)$, $V(c,0)$

7. $J(2a,0)$

8. B

9. D

10. $\left(\dfrac{a}{2},b\right)$

11. $\left(\dfrac{a}{2},\dfrac{b}{2}\right)$

12. $OP = 3$

13. D

14. total area $= 176$

15. volume $= 16$ in.^{3}

16. slope $= -\dfrac{2}{3}$

17. slope $= \dfrac{5}{3}$

18. C

19. C

20. area $= 36$

21. $s = 6$

22. B

23. Rectangle *FGHJ* (Given). Now, we know by the Distance Formula that $FH = \sqrt{(a-0)^2+(b-0)^2} = \sqrt{a^2+b^2}$. The Distance Formula also allows us to say that $GJ = \sqrt{(0-a)^2+(b-0)^2} = \sqrt{(-a)^2+(b)^2} = \sqrt{a^2+b^2}$. So by the Transitive Property, we know that $FH = GJ$.

24. Right triangle *ABC*; *D* is the midpoint of $\overline{BC}$ (Given). By the Midpoint Formula, the coordinates of point *D* are $\left(\dfrac{0+a}{2},\dfrac{b+0}{2}\right)$ or $\left(\dfrac{a}{2},\dfrac{b}{2}\right)$. Then by the Distance Formula, $AD = \sqrt{\left(\dfrac{a}{2}-0\right)^2+\left(\dfrac{b}{2}-0\right)^2} = \sqrt{\left(\dfrac{a}{2}\right)^2+\left(\dfrac{b}{2}\right)^2} = \sqrt{\dfrac{a^2}{4}+\dfrac{b^2}{4}}$ $= \sqrt{\dfrac{a^2+b^2}{4}} = \dfrac{\sqrt{a^2+b^2}}{2}$. Similarly, by the Distance Formula, $BD = \sqrt{\left(\dfrac{a}{2}-0\right)^2+\left(\dfrac{b}{2}-b\right)^2}$ $= \sqrt{\left(\dfrac{a}{2}-0\right)^2+\left(\dfrac{b}{2}-\dfrac{2b}{2}\right)^2} = \sqrt{\left(\dfrac{a}{2}\right)^2+\left(-\dfrac{b}{2}\right)^2}$ $= \sqrt{\dfrac{a^2}{4}+\dfrac{b^2}{4}} = \sqrt{\dfrac{a^2+b^2}{4}} = \dfrac{\sqrt{a^2+b^2}}{2}$. Finally, by the Transitive Property $AD = BD$.

Practice 106

a. area $= 5$

b. volume $= 160$ cm^3

c. A

d. perimeter $= 32$

e. $\odot O$ with center at (3, 3) and radius 2 (Given). Any intersection points are solutions to the system: $\begin{cases} y = x+2 \\ (x-3)^2+(y-3)^2 = 4 \end{cases}$.

Substituting $x+2$ in for *y*:

$(x-3)^2+(x+2-3)^2 = 4$

$(x-3)^2+(x-1)^2 = 4$

$x^2-3x-3x+9+x^2-x-x+1 = 4$

$x^2-6x+9+x^2-2x+1 = 4$

$2x^2-8x+10 = 4$

$x^2-4x+5 = 2$

$x^2-4x+3 = 0$

$(x-3)(x-1) = 0$

$x-3 = 0$ and $x-1 = 0$

$x = 3$ and $x = 1$.

Substituting these *x* values into the equation $y = x+2$ we get $y = 5$ and $y = 3$ so the solutions are (3, 5) and (1, 3). Since the system has two solutions, the line intersects the circle in two points and is therefore a secant line.

Problem Set 106

1. False

2. True

3. C

4. B

5. C

6. $OP = \sqrt{13}$, $PQ = 3$

7. $OA = 5$

8. area $= 10$

9. area $= 10$

10. total area $= 740$

11. volume $= 1{,}280$ cm^3

12. volume $= 405\pi$

13. $PR = \dfrac{3}{4}$

14. $HL = 8$

15. slope $= -\dfrac{5}{2}$

16. slope $= \dfrac{7}{6}$

17. A

18. D

19. E

20. $z = \sqrt{170}$

21. $x = 72$

22. perimeter $= 16$

23. Quadrilateral $ABCD$ (Given). $AD = a$ and $BC = a + b - b = a$ (The length of a horizontal line segment is the absolute value of the difference in the x values of its end points.), so $AD = BC$ by substitution. Next, by the Distance Formula, $AB = \sqrt{(b-0)^2 + (c-0)^2}$ $= \sqrt{b^2 + c^2}$. Also by the Distance Formula, $DC = \sqrt{(a+b-a)^2 + (c-0)^2} = \sqrt{b^2 + c^2}$. So by the Transitive Property $AB = DC$.

24. $\odot O$ with center at (3, 2) and radius 2 (Given). Any intersection points are solutions to the system: $\begin{cases} y = x + 1 \\ (x-3)^2 + (y-2)^2 = 4 \end{cases}$.

Substituting $x + 1$ in for y:

$(x-3)^2 + (x+1-2)^2 = 4$

$(x-3)^2 + (x-1)^2 = 4$

$x^2 - 3x - 3x + 9 + x^2 - x - x + 1 = 4$

$x^2 - 6x + 9 + x^2 - 2x + 1 = 4$

$2x^2 - 8x + 10 = 4$

$x^2 - 4x + 5 = 2$

$x^2 - 4x + 3 = 0$

$(x-3)(x-1) = 0$

$x - 3 = 0$ and $x - 1 = 0$

$x = 3$ and $x = 1$.

Substituting these x values into the equation $y = x + 1$ we get $y = 4$ and $y = 2$, so the solutions are (3, 4) and (1, 2). Since the system has two solutions, the line intersects the circle in two points and is therefore a secant line.p

CHAPTER 16

Practice 107

a. B

b. $64:125$

c. D

d. $y = 60$

e. $\triangle PQR$; S is the midpoint of $\overline{PQ}$ (Given). By the Midpoint Formula, the coordinates of S are $\left(\dfrac{a}{2}, \dfrac{b}{2}\right)$. Also, T is the midpoint of $\overline{QR}$ (Given) and by the Midpoint Formula, the coordinates of T are $\left(\dfrac{a+d}{2}, \dfrac{b}{2}\right)$. Next, the slope of $\overline{ST}$ is

$$\dfrac{\dfrac{b}{2}-\dfrac{b}{2}}{\dfrac{a+d}{2}-\dfrac{a}{2}} = 0.$$ The slope of $\overline{PR}$ is $\dfrac{0-0}{d-0} = 0$.

Since their slopes are equal, $\overline{ST} \parallel \overline{PR}$. And since $\overline{PR}$ and $\overline{ST}$ are horizontal, the length of each is the absolute value of the difference in the x values of their end points. So, $ST = \dfrac{a+d}{2} - \dfrac{a}{2} = \dfrac{d}{2}$ and $PR = d-0 = d$.

Finally, we know that $\dfrac{1}{2}PR = \dfrac{d}{2}$. Therefore, by the Transitive Property, $ST = \dfrac{1}{2}PR$.

Problem Set 107

1. True

2. True

3. C

4. E

5. B

6. $B(a,d)$, $D(c,b)$

7. $L(0,b)$, $J(b,b)$

8. D

9. $(-2,-2)$

10. D

11. A

12. A

13. total area $= 356$ cm^2

14. $27:343$

15. area $= 18$

16. B

17. A

18. D

19. $x = 127$

20. $y = 54$

21. C

22. D

23. Isosceles trapezoid $FGHJ$ (Given). Draw diagonals $\overline{FH}$ and $\overline{GJ}$. By the Distance Formula, $FH = \sqrt{(c-0)^2 + (b-0)^2} = \sqrt{c^2+b^2}$. Also by the Distance Formula, $GJ = \sqrt{(a+c-a)^2 + (0-b)^2} = \sqrt{c^2+b^2}$. Finally, by the Transitive Property, $FH = GJ$. So the diagonals are congruent.

24. $\triangle ABC$; D is the midpoint of $\overline{AB}$ (Given). By the Midpoint Formula, the coordinates of D are $\left(\dfrac{a}{2}, \dfrac{b}{2}\right)$. Also, E is the midpoint of $\overline{BC}$ (Given). And by the Midpoint Formula, the coordinates of E are $\left(\dfrac{a+c}{2}, \dfrac{b}{2}\right)$. Next, the slope of $\overline{DE}$ is $\dfrac{\dfrac{b}{2}-\dfrac{b}{2}}{\dfrac{a+c}{2}-\dfrac{a}{2}} = 0$ and the slope of $\overline{AC}$ is $\dfrac{0-0}{c-0} = 0$. Since their slopes are equal, $\overline{DE} \parallel \overline{AC}$. And since $\overline{AC}$ and $\overline{DE}$ are horizontal, the length of each is the absolute value of the difference in the x values of their end points. So, $DE = \dfrac{a+c}{2} - \dfrac{a}{2} = \dfrac{c}{2}$ and $AC = c-0 = c$. Finally, we know that $\dfrac{1}{2}AC = \dfrac{c}{2}$. Therefore, by the Transitive Property, $DE = \dfrac{1}{2}AC$.

Practice 108

a. B

b. C

c. $T(a, a\sqrt{3})$

d. A

e. Trapezoid $EFGH$; I is the midpoint of $\overline{EF}$ (Given). By the Midpoint Formula, I has coordinates (b,c). J is the midpoint of $\overline{GH}$ (Given). Also by the Midpoint Formula, J has coordinates $(d+a,c)$. Subtracting x-coordinates, the horizontal distances are $IJ =$

$d + a - b$, $EH = 2a$, and $FG = 2d - 2b$. (The length of a horizontal line segment is the absolute value of the difference in x values of its end points.) So by substitution, $\frac{1}{2}(EH + FG)$

$= \frac{1}{2}(2a + 2d - 2b) = a + d - b = d + a - b = IJ$. Finally, by the Transitive Property, we know that $IJ = \frac{1}{2}(EH + FG)$.

Problem Set 108

1. True
2. False
3. A
4. B
5. E
6. $OQ = 17$
7. C
8. B
9. A
10. C
11. A
12. E
13. D
14. surface area $= 96\pi$ m^2
15. A
16. B
17. D
18. D
19. $A(-a, 0)$, $B(0, a\sqrt{3})$
20. E
21. area $= 960$ cm^2
22. area $= 960$ in.^{2}
23. Rhombus $OPQR$ (Given). Draw the diagonals $\overline{PR}$ and $\overline{OQ}$. The slope of $\overline{PR}$ is $\frac{4-0}{3-5} =$

$\frac{4}{-2} = -2$. The slope of $\overline{OQ}$ is $\frac{4-0}{8-0} = \frac{4}{8} = \frac{1}{2}$.

Since the slopes -2 and $\frac{1}{2}$ are negative reciprocals, $\overline{PR} \perp \overline{OQ}$.

24. Trapezoid $ABCD$; E is the midpoint of $\overline{AB}$ (Given). By the Midpoint Formula, E has coordinates (a, b). F is the midpoint of $\overline{CD}$ (Given). Also by the Midpoint Formula, F has coordinates $(c + d, b)$. If we subtract the x-coordinates, then the horizontal distances are $EF = c + d - a$, $AD = 2d - 0 = 2d$, and

$BC = 2c - 2a$. (The length of a horizontal line segment is the absolute value of the difference in x values of its end points.) So by substitution,

$\frac{1}{2}(AD + BC) = \frac{1}{2}(2d + 2c - 2a) = d + c - a$

$= c + d - a = EF$. Therefore, by the Transitive Property, $EF = \frac{1}{2}(AD + BC)$.

Practice 109

a. B
b. $4\sqrt{2}$
c. C
d. $JK = 6\sqrt{3}$ cm
e.

Statements	Reasons
1. $\overline{PQ}$ is a diameter of $\odot O$.	1. Given
2. $\angle PSQ$ is a right angle.	2. An inscribed angle that intercepts a semicircle is a right angle.
3. $m\angle PSQ = 90$	3. Definition of a right angle
4. $m\angle PRQ > m\angle PSQ$	4. The measure of an exterior angle of a triangle is greater than the measure of either of the remote interior angles.
5. $m\angle PRQ > 90$	5. Substitution Property of Inequality
6. $\angle PRQ$ is obtuse.	6. Definition of an obtuse angle
7. $\triangle PRQ$ is obtuse.	7. Definition of an obtuse triangle

Problem Set 109

1. True
2. True
3. C
4. D
5. A
6. slope $= -\frac{1}{2}$
7. slope $= \frac{b}{a}$
8. D

9. E
10. A
11. B
12. 13
13. E
14. C
15. $m\angle A = 28$; $m\angle B = 96$; $m\angle C = 56$
16. $m\angle Q = 23$; $m\angle O = 134$; $m\angle R = 23$
17. D
18. E
19. $MN = 3$ cm
20. $LM = 3\sqrt{3}$ cm
21. perimeter = 42
22. The 18-inch pizza
23.

Statements	Reasons
1. $\widehat{JK} \cong \widehat{KL}$	1. Given
2. $\angle JMK \cong \angle KJL$	2. Inscribed angles that intercept congruent arcs are congruent.
3. $\angle JKN \cong \angle JKN$	3. Reflexive Property
4. $\triangle JKN \sim \triangle MKJ$	4. Angle-Angle Similarity

24.

Statements	Reasons
1. $\overline{AC}$ is a diameter of $\odot O$.	1. Given
2. $\angle ADC$ is a right angle.	2. An inscribed angle that intercepts a semicircle is a right angle.
3. $m\angle ADC = 90$	3. Definition of a right angle
4. $m\angle ABC > m\angle ADC$	4. The measure of an exterior angle of a triangle is greater than the measure of either of the remote interior angles.
5. $m\angle ABC > 90$	5. Substitution Property of Inequality
6. $\angle ABC$ is obtuse.	6. Definition of an obtuse angle
7. $\triangle ABC$ is obtuse.	7. Definition of an obtuse triangle

Practice 110
a. area = 2π
b. A
c. $EG = 9\sqrt{3}$ in.

d. area = 8
e.

Statements	Reasons
1. $\overline{CO}$ is a diameter of $\odot P$; $\overline{AC}$ is a chord of $\odot O$.	1. Given
2. $\angle CBO$ is a right angle.	2. An inscribed angle that intercepts a semicircle is a right angle.
3. $\overline{OB} \perp \overline{AC}$	3. Definition of perpendicular lines
4. $AB = BC$	4. If a line through the center of a circle is perpendicular to a chord, it also bisects the chord.

Problem Set 110
1. True
2. True
3. B
4. D
5. C
6. A
7. $PQ = 2a$
8. C
9. E
10. A
11. B
12. $2\sqrt{10}$
13. A
14. E
15. volume = 1,680 in.^{3}
16. volume = 32π ft.^{3}
17. E
18. D
19. $AC = 6\sqrt{3}$ in.
20. $AD = 9$ in.
21. area = 50
22. area = 80π
23.

Statements	Reasons
1. Chords $\overline{CF}$ and $\overline{DG}$ intersect at point E.	1. Given
2. $\angle G \cong \angle F$ and $\angle C \cong \angle D$	2. Inscribed angles that intercept the same arc are congruent.
3. $\triangle GCE \sim \triangle FDE$	3. Angle-Angle Similarity

| 4. | $\dfrac{CG}{DF} = \dfrac{GE}{FE}$ | 4. Converse of the definition of similar triangles |

24.

	Statements	Reasons
1.	$\overline{QP}$ is a diameter of $\odot O$; $\overline{QS}$ is a chord of $\odot P$.	1. Given
2.	$\angle QRP$ is a right angle.	2. An inscribed angle that intercepts a semicircle is a right angle.
3.	$\overline{PR} \perp \overline{QS}$	3. Definition of perpendicular lines
4.	$QR = RS$	4. If a line through the center of a circle is perpendicular to a chord, it also bisects the chord.

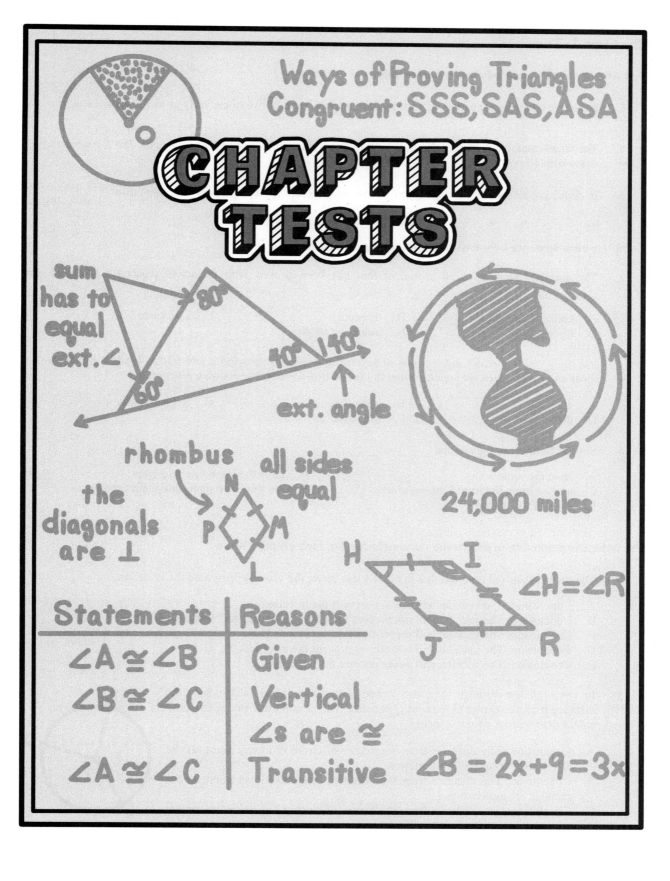

Ways of Proving Triangles
Congruent: SSS, SAS, ASA

CHAPTER TESTS

sum has to equal ext. ∠

80°

40° 140°

60°

↑ ext. angle

rhombus

the diagonals are ⊥

all sides equal

N

P   M

L

24,000 miles

H   I

J   R

∠H = ∠R

Statements	Reasons
∠A ≅ ∠B	Given
∠B ≅ ∠C	Vertical ∠s are ≅
∠A ≅ ∠C	Transitive

∠B = 2x + 9 = 3x

Chapter 1 Test

Tell whether each sentence below is true or false.

1.
(1)
Inductive reasoning, the method used by the Egyptians and Babylonians, only gives probable facts.

2.
(5)
The Greek mathematician Euclid decided to use only inductive reasoning in his book *The Elements*, which starts with 10 postulates.

3.
(2)
In deductive reasoning, as long as you've reasoned correctly, the conclusion *has* to be true.

Complete each sentence below with the best of the choices given.

4.
(4)
The final conclusion of an argument that has been proven with deductive reasoning is called a(n) _____.

    A. geometrical complexity   B. theorem   C. syllogism
    D. direct proof   E. inductive statement

5.
(1)
In _____ reasoning we look at several examples of something and find a fact that holds true for those examples. Then we conclude that the fact is true for all other possible examples.

    A. algebraic   B. geometric   C. trigonometric
    D. deductive   E. inductive

6.
(5)
Similar figures are figures that _____.

    A. have the same area   B. have the same line thickness
    C. are the same shape and the same size   D. are the same shape and different size
    E. none of the above

Use inductive reasoning to determine the conclusion for each premise below.

7.
(1)
The medical journal reported that in all 184 test cases, the vaccine prevented the infection.

    A. Conclusion: The vaccine will always prevent the infection.
    B. Conclusion: The vaccine will not prevent the infection in the 185th test case.
    C. Conclusion: The vaccine will prevent 184 different infections.
    D. Conclusion: The vaccine will sometimes prevent the infection.
    E. Conclusion: The vaccine will never prevent the infection.

8.
(1)
In circle *O*, the distance from the center *O* to point *P* equals 2 inches, the distance from the center *O* to point *Q* equals 2 inches, and the distance from the center *O* to point *R* equals 2 inches.

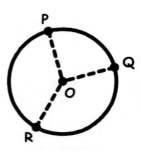

    A. Conclusion: The distance from the center of circle *O* to any point on the circle always equals 2 millimeters.
    B. Conclusion: The distance from the center of circle *O* to any point on the circle is always changing.
    C. Conclusion: The distance from the center of circle *O* to any point on the circle is always equal to 2 inches.
    D. Conclusion: The distance from the center of circle *O* to any point on the circle sometimes changes.
    E. Conclusion: The distance between any two points on circle *O* always equals 2 inches.

Select the premise and the conclusion of the conditional statement below.

9.
(2) If a team has only an inch to go on fourth down, then they absolutely must go for it.

    A. Premise: If they absolutely must go for it
        Conclusion: then a team has only an inch to go on fourth down

    B. Premise: If a team has only an inch to go on fourth down
        Conclusion: then they absolutely must go for it

Rewrite the sentence below in conditional ("if-then") form and select the proper answer.

10.
(2) All runaway grocery carts hate it when the parking lot slopes upward.

    A. If you hate it when the parking lot slopes upward, then you are a runaway grocery cart.
    B. If you like it when the parking lot slopes downward, then you are a runaway grocery cart.
    C. If you are a runaway grocery cart, then you hate it when the parking lot slopes upward.
    D. If you are a runaway grocery cart, then you like it when the parking lot slopes upward.
    E. If you are a grocery cart, then you hate it when the parking lot slopes upward.

Select the Venn diagram that represents each set of conditional statements below.

11.
(2) If a being is a Venusian, then it is six legged. If QZ3 is a Venusian, then QZ3 is six legged.

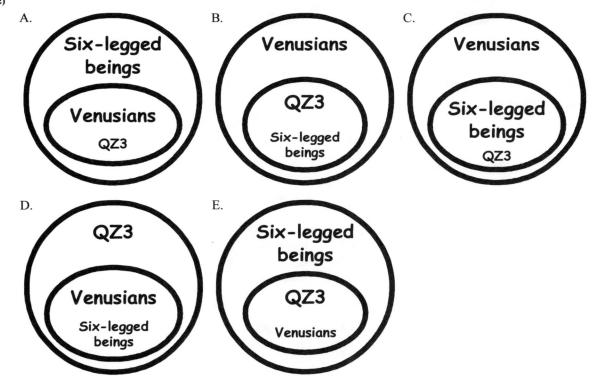

12. All male pink flamingos wish they were blue. Pauley is a male pink flamingo. So Pauley wishes he was blue.
(2)

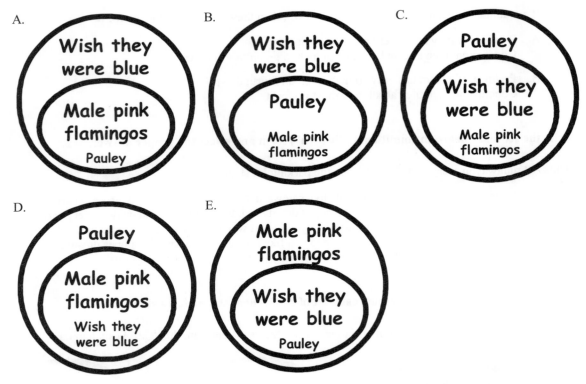

A.

B.

C.

D.

E.

Select the set of conditional statements that represents each Venn diagram below.

13.
(2)

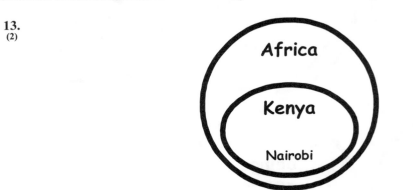

A. If a city is in Africa, then it is in Kenya. If Nairobi is in Kenya, then it is in Africa.

B. If a city is in Kenya, then it is in Africa. If Nairobi is a city, then it is in Africa.

C. If Nairobi is a city, then it is in Kenya. If Kenya is in Africa, then Nairobi is in Africa.

D. If Nairobi is in Kenya, then it is a city. If Kenya is in Africa, then Nairobi is in Africa.

E. If a city is in Kenya, then it is in Africa. If Nairobi is in Kenya, then it is in Africa.

14.
(2)

A. If an orchestra member plays the triangle, then he definitely feels underappreciated. If Lester feels underappreciated, then he definitely plays the triangle.

B. If an orchestra member feels underappreciated, then he definitely plays the triangle. If Lester feels underappreciated, then he definitely plays the triangle.

C. If an orchestra member plays the triangle, then he definitely feels underappreciated. If Lester is an orchestra member, then he definitely feels underappreciated.

D. If an orchestra member plays the triangle, then he definitely feels underappreciated. If Lester is the orchestra's triangle player, then he definitely feels underappreciated.

E. If an orchestra member feels underappreciated, then he definitely plays the triangle. If Lester is an orchestra member, then he definitely plays the triangle.

Tell whether each argument below is an example of inductive or deductive reasoning.

15. If all the people at Maria's party are 15 years old, and if Sandra is at Maria's party, then Sandra must be 15
(2) years old.

16. If the first 3 bull-riding contestants wore cowboy hats, then all of the bull-riding contestants will wear
(2) cowboy hats.

Tell whether the arguments below are valid or invalid deductions.

17. Since all pearl divers know how to swim and Suzy knows how to swim, Suzy must be a pearl diver.
(2)

18. All teenagers have bad hair days and Chloe is a teenager, so Chloe has bad hair days.
(2)

Use deductive reasoning to select a conclusion for each set of statements below.

19. If a man is batting in the cleanup position, then he better be a slugger. If Gary hopes to bat in the cleanup
(2) position one day, _____.

    A. then he better not strike out   B. then he better know how to steal bases
    C. then he better become a slugger   D. then he better not have any injuries
    E. then Gary is currently a pitcher

20. All elephants are afraid of mice, and Jumbo is an elephant. Therefore, _____.
(2)

    A. Jumbo is unafraid of mice
    B. Jumbo is the only elephant that is afraid of mice
    C. Jumbo is the only elephant that is unafraid of mice
    D. all mice are afraid of elephants
    E. Jumbo is afraid of mice

Select the choice that (when put in the blank) will create a fact that fits with the conclusion. Assume inductive reasoning is being used.

21. The police officer _____ of the first five drivers who stopped at the traffic light.
(1)

Conclusion: The police officer shined his flashlight in the faces of all the drivers who stopped at the traffic light.

    A. shined his flashlight in the faces   B. pulled over each
    C. gave warnings to each   D. disregarded each
    E. shined his flashlight in the cars

Select the theorem that is proved by the statements below.

22. If the scoop falls off the cone, the car seat will get messy.
(4) If the car seat gets messy, the driver will become distracted.
If the driver becomes distracted, he will swerve off the road.
If the driver swerves off the road, he will hit the fire hydrant.

    A. Theorem: If the driver swerves off the road, he will hit the fire hydrant.
    B. Theorem: If the scoop falls off the cone, the driver will hit the fire hydrant.
    C. Theorem: If the scoop falls off the cone, the car seat will get messy.
    D. Theorem: If the car seat gets messy, the driver will swerve off the road.
    E. Theorem: If the scoop falls off the cone, the driver will become distracted.

Complete a direct proof for each theorem by rearranging the statements in logical order.

23. Theorem: If the bride stares for too long into the groom's eyes, Brenda won't get married next.
(4)

If the cake-cutting is delayed by half an hour, then Brenda, one of the bridesmaids, will have to leave early.
If she does not catch the bouquet, Brenda won't get married next.
If Brenda leaves early, she will not catch the bouquet.
If the bride stares for too long into the groom's eyes, she will delay the cutting of the cake by half an hour.

24. Theorem: If Mom drops her pots and pans, all the neighbors will wake up.
(4)

If the baby begins to cry, the dog will start to bark.
If the pots and pans hit the floor, the baby will begin to cry.
If Mom drops her pots and pans, they will hit the floor.
If the dog starts to bark, all the neighbors will wake up.

Chapter 2 Test

Tell whether each sentence below is true or false.

1.
(6)   In geometry every single term must be defined.

2.
(7)   Collinear points are points that lie on the same line.

3.
(11)   All obtuse angles are congruent.

Complete each sentence below with the best of the choices given.

4.
(6)   A _____ is a set of points that forms a flat surface which extends forever in all directions and has length and width, but no depth.

    A. bisector   B. line   C. plane
    D. vertex   E. ray

5.
(12) $\overrightarrow{BD}$ is the _____ of $\angle ABC$ if D lies in the interior of $\angle ABC$ and $m\angle ABD = m\angle DBC$.

    A. line segment   B. midpoint   C. ray
    D. bisector   E. midline

6.
(9)   An angle's end point is called the _____ of the angle.

    A. coordinate   B. side   C. vertex
    D. degree   E. origin

7.
(7)   _____ determine(s) a unique straight line.

    A. Three noncollinear points
    B. Two points
    C. An end point and the set of all points on one side of it
    D. One point
    E. Two angles

Complete each sentence below with the best of the choices given and determine the property being described.

8.
(13)   If equals are _____ equals, the results are _____ : If $a = b$, then $ac = bc$.

    A. divided by; equal; Transitive Property   B. added to; unequal; Addition Property
    C. substituted for; equal; Substitution Property   D. subtracted from; equal; Subtraction Property
    E. multiplied by; equal; Multiplication Property

9.
(13)   If $a = b$, then either a or b may be _____ the other in any equation.

    A. substituted for; Substitution Property   B. added to; Transitive Property
    C. multiplied by; Reflexive Property   D. subtracted from; Substitution Property
    E. substituted for; Reflexive Property

Select the answer to each question below.

10. Which choice correctly tells what each of the symbols below could represent?
(9)

$$\overline{GH} \qquad\qquad \angle W \qquad\qquad \overrightarrow{ST}$$

A. $\overrightarrow{GH}$ is a ray, $\angle W$ is an angle, and $\overrightarrow{ST}$ is a line segment.
B. $\overline{GH}$ is a line segment, $\angle W$ is an angle, and $\overrightarrow{ST}$ is a ray.
C. $\overleftrightarrow{GH}$ is a line, $\angle W$ is an angle, and $\overrightarrow{ST}$ is a ray.
D. $\overline{GH}$ is a line segment, $\angle W$ is a bisector, and $\overrightarrow{ST}$ is a ray.
E. $\overline{GH}$ is a line segment, $\angle W$ is an angle, and $\overleftrightarrow{ST}$ is a line.

11. How many end points does a line segment have? a ray? a line?
(9)
   A. None; One; None   B. Two; Two; Two   C. Two; One; Two
   D. Two; One; None   E. One; None; One

Select the Venn diagram that represents the set of statements below.

12. To pass your driver's test, you have to stop at all red lights. Ramona passed her driver's test, so she must
(2)   have stopped at all red lights.

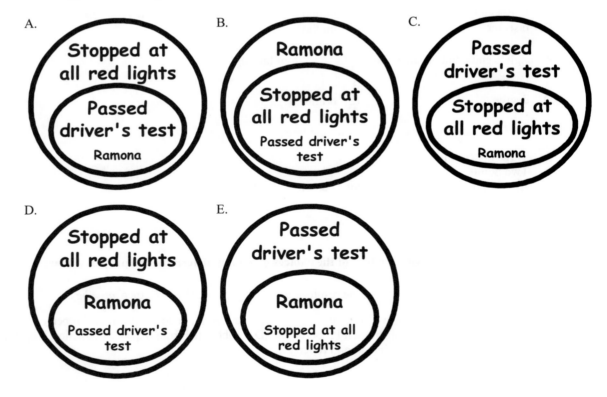

98

Select the set of conditional statements that represents the Venn diagram below.

13.
(2)

A. If you are a true mountain man, then your beard goes all the way down to your chest. If Travis is a true mountain man, then his beard goes all the way down to his chest.

B. If you are a true mountain man, then your beard goes all the way down to your chest. If Travis's beard goes all the way down to his chest, then he is a true mountain man.

C. If your beard goes all the way down to your chest, then you are a true mountain man. If Travis's beard goes all the way down to his chest, then he is a true mountain man.

D. If you are a man, then your beard goes all the way down to your chest. If Travis is a man, then his beard goes all the way down to his chest.

E. If your beard goes all the way down to your chest, then you are a true mountain man. If Travis is a true mountain man, then his beard goes all the way down to his chest.

Use Betweenness of Points or Rays to answer each question below.

14. If point A lies in the interior of $\angle BCD$ and if $m\angle BCA = 22$, $m\angle BCD = 105$, and $m\angle ACD = 83$, then
(10) which of the following rays is between the other two?

A. $\overrightarrow{CB}$ is between $\overrightarrow{CA}$ and $\overrightarrow{CD}$.   B. $\overrightarrow{CA}$ is between $\overrightarrow{CB}$ and $\overrightarrow{CD}$.

C. $\overrightarrow{CD}$ is between $\overrightarrow{CA}$ and $\overrightarrow{CB}$.

15. If K-L-M (point L is between points K and M), and if $KM = 11\frac{1}{4}$ and $KL = 3\frac{1}{2}$, then find LM.
(8)

Use the definition of a segment or angle bisector to answer each question below.

16. If $\overrightarrow{VW}$ bisects $\overline{PS}$ at point V, and if $PS = 29.2$, then find PV.
(12)

17. If $\overrightarrow{NQ}$ bisects $\angle MNP$, and if $m\angle QNM = 67$, then find $m\angle MNP$.
(12)

Select the answer to the question below.

18. Name the obtuse angle in the diagram. Then measure $\angle GJF$ with a protractor and tell what kind of angle
(11) it is.

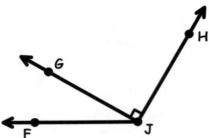

A. $\angle FJH$ (or $\angle HJF$); 27°; acute

C. $\angle FJG$ (or $\angle GJF$); 153°; obtuse

E. $\angle FJH$ (or $\angle HJF$); 117°; obtuse

B. $\angle GJH$ (or $\angle HJG$); 90°; right

D. $\angle GJH$ (or $\angle HJG$); 27°; acute

Tell whether the arguments below are valid or invalid deductions.

19. All fish have gills, and all sharks are fish. Therefore, all sharks have gills.
(2)

20. Pam wears goofy outfits. All mascots for professional sports teams wear goofy outfits, so Pam must be a
(2) mascot for a professional sports team.

Use deductive reasoning to select the conclusion for the statement below.

21. If a bona fide soprano can shatter glass with her voice and if Beverly is a bona fide soprano, then
(2) _____.

A. Conclusion: anyone who can shatter glass with her voice is a bona fide soprano

B. Conclusion: everybody can shatter glass with their voice

C. Conclusion: she can shatter glass with her voice

D. Conclusion: she sings in the opera

E. Conclusion: she cannot shatter glass with her voice

Complete a direct proof for the theorem below by rearranging the statements in logical order.

22. Theorem: If the explorer's hunch is wrong, then he and the crew will end up eating shoe leather for
(4) breakfast.

If his map is off by 1,000 miles, he and his crew will run out of food before they reach the islands.
If they run out of food before they reach the islands, they will all begin to starve.
If the explorer's hunch is wrong, then his map will be off by 1,000 miles.
If the explorer and his crew begin to starve, they will end up eating shoe leather for breakfast.

Select the reverse of each definition below and tell whether it passes the reversibility test.

23.
(7)
Michelangelo was a famous artist.

   A. A famous artist was Michelangelo; passes
   B. The most famous artist was Michelangelo; does not pass
   C. Famous artists are named Michelangelo; passes
   D. A famous artist was Michelangelo; does not pass
   E. Famous artists are named Michelangelo; does not pass

24.
(7)
A BLT is a sandwich containing only bacon, lettuce, and tomato.

   A. The only sandwich containing bacon, lettuce, and tomato is a BLT; passes
   B. A sandwich containing only bacon, lettuce, and tomato is a BLT; does not pass
   C. A sandwich containing only bacon, lettuce, and tomato is a BLT; passes
   D. The only sandwich containing bacon, lettuce, and tomato is a BLT; does not pass
   E. All sandwiches with bacon, lettuce, and tomato are BLTs; passes

Chapter 3 Test

Tell whether each sentence below is true or false.

1.
(18)
Vertical angles are a pair of adjacent angles whose exterior sides form a straight line.

2.
(20)
Through a given point *not* on a line, there exists exactly one perpendicular to the given line.

Complete each sentence below with the best of the choices given.

3.
(16)
_____ angles are angles with measures that add to equal 180.

A. Complementary
B. Supplementary
C. Adjacent
D. Vertical
E. Obtuse

4.
(18)
Vertical angles are a pair of _____ angles formed by two intersecting lines.

A. nonadjacent
B. supplementary
C. right
D. adjacent
E. acute

5.
(16)
If two angles are supplementary to the same angle or equal (congruent) angles, then they are _____.

A. equal
B. adjacent
C. vertical
D. unique
E. a linear pair

6.
(20)
If the exterior sides of a pair of adjacent angles are perpendicular, the angles are _____.

A. congruent
B. right angles
C. supplementary
D. a linear pair
E. complementary

Use a ruler to measure the distance below (in inches) and then select your answer from the choices.

7.
(21)
the distance between point *P* and line *n*

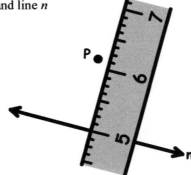

A. approximately 1 inch
B. approximately $1\frac{3}{4}$ inches
C. approximately $1\frac{1}{2}$ inches

D. approximately $1\frac{1}{8}$ inches
E. approximately $\frac{7}{8}$ of an inch

From each given statement below, select the definition, property, postulate, or theorem that justifies each prove statement.

8. Given: Lines $\overrightarrow{JK}$ and $\overrightarrow{LM}$ intersect at point N.
(18)   Prove: $\angle JNM \cong \angle KNL$

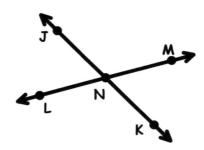

   A. Betweenness of Rays
   B. If two angles are complementary to the same angle, then they are congruent.
   C. Pairs of vertical angles are congruent.
   D. Definition of congruent angles
   E. If two angles are a linear pair, then they are congruent.

9. Given: $\angle JNL$ and $\angle LNK$ are a linear pair.
(17)   Prove: $\angle JNL$ and $\angle LNK$ are supplementary.

   A. If two angles are supplementary to the same angle, then they are congruent.
   B. Definition of supplementary angles
   C. If two angles are vertical angles, then they are supplementary.
   D. If two angles are adjacent, then they are supplementary.
   E. If two angles are a linear pair, then they are supplementary.

10. Given: $\angle X$ and $\angle Y$ are supplementary; $\angle Y$ and $\angle Z$ are supplementary.
(16)   Prove: $\angle X \cong \angle Z$

   A. Transitive Property
   B. If two angles are supplementary to the same angle, then they are congruent.
   C. Reflexive Property
   D. Definition of supplementary angles
   E. Definition of congruent angles

Find the measures of the complement and supplement of each angle below.

11. $m\angle PQR = 37$
(16)

12. $m\angle E = 90 - x$
(16)
   A. complement: x
      supplement: $90 + x$

   B. complement: $180 - x$
      supplement: $90 - x$

   C. complement: $90 - x$
      supplement: $180 - x$

   D. complement: $x - 90$
      supplement: $x - 180$

   E. complement: $90 + x$
      supplement: x

Use the definition of a segment or angle bisector to answer each question below.

13. If $\overline{CE}$ bisects $\angle BCD$, and if $m\angle BCE = 3x - 6$ and $m\angle ECD = 2x + 11$, find $m\angle BCD$. Is $\angle BCD$ acute,
(12) right, or obtuse?

    A. $m\angle BCD = 73$; obtuse   B. $m\angle BCD = 45$; acute   C. $m\angle BCD = 90$; right

    D. $m\angle BCD = 42$; acute   E. $m\angle BCD = 17$; acute

14. If $\overline{IJ}$ bisects $\overline{GH}$ at point J, and if $GJ = 3y - 1$ and $JH = 2y + 7$, find GH.
(12)

Answer the question below.

15. Using the diagram, tell whether the listed angle pairs are "adjacent" or "not adjacent."
(17)

$\angle RST$ and $\angle TSU$

$\angle TSU$ and $\angle UVW$

Find the measure of each angle below.

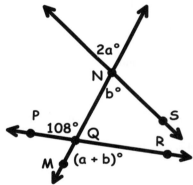

16. $\angle PQM$
(17)

17. $\angle QNS$
(18)

Answer each question below.

18. An angle's measure is 18 more than 3 times its complement. Find the measure of the angle.
(15)

19. The supplement of an angle is 4 times as large as the angle's complement. Find the measure of the angle.
(16)

Complete the sentence below with *always*, *sometimes*, or *never*.

20. Adjacent angles are _____ supplementary.
(17)

    A. always   B. sometimes   C. never

Tell whether the arguments below are valid or invalid deductions.

21. If two angles are a linear pair, then they are supplementary. $\angle A$ and $\angle B$ are supplementary. Therefore,
(2) $\angle A$ and $\angle B$ are a linear pair.

22. Pairs of vertical angles are congruent. $\angle 1$ and $\angle 3$ are not congruent, so they are not a pair of vertical angles.
(2)

Complete the proof below by filling in the blanks.

23. Given: $m\angle LIK = m\angle LJK$; $\overline{IJ}$ bisects $\angle LIK$; $\overline{IJ}$ bisects $\angle LJK$.

Prove: $m\angle 1 = m\angle 2$

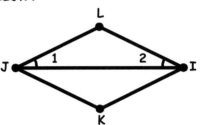

Statements	Reasons
1. $\overline{IJ}$ bisects $\angle LIK$	1. Given
2.	2. Given
3. $m\angle 2 = \dfrac{1}{2}m\angle LIK$	3.
4.	4. Definition of an angle bisector
5. $m\angle LIK = m\angle LJK$	5.
6. $\dfrac{1}{2}m\angle LIK = \dfrac{1}{2}m\angle LJK$	6.
7.	7. Substitution Property

Do the proof below.

24. Given: $\angle 3$ is complementary to $\angle 1$; $\angle 4$ is complementary to $\angle 2$.
Prove: $m\angle 1 = m\angle 2$

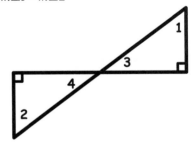

Chapter 4 Test

Tell whether each sentence below is true or false.

1. When the "if" clause and "then" clause of a statement are flipped around, the "converse" of the original
(26) statement is created.

2. If two parallel lines are cut by a transversal, then interior angles on the same side of the transversal are
(24) supplementary.

Complete each sentence below with the best of the choices given.

3. A _____ is a line that intersects two or more lines in different points.
(22)
    A. bisector   B. perpendicular bisector   C. segment bisector
    D. transversal   E. divisor line

4. $\overleftrightarrow{EF} \parallel \overleftrightarrow{GH}$ means that _____.
(22)
    A. lines EF and GH are parallel   B. lines EF and GH are congruent
    C. lines EF and GH are perpendicular   D. lines EF and GH are adjacent
    E. lines EF and GH intersect

5. If two lines form congruent alternate interior angles with a transversal, then the lines _____.
(26)
    A. are congruent   B. form four right angles   C. are parallel
    D. intersect   E. are perpendicular

6. A good definition is one where both the original statement and the _____ are true.
(26)
    A. reflexive   B. modifying statement   C. converse
    D. conclusion   E. thesis

Decide whether each definition below passes the reversibility test by writing its converse and determining whether the converse is true. Then, select your answer.

7. If two angles are a linear pair, then the sum of their measures is 180.
(26)
    A. If the sum of the measures of two angles is 180, then the angles form a linear pair; Converse is true and the definition passes.
    B. If each of the measures of two angles is 180, then the angles form a linear pair; Converse is not true and the definition does not pass.
    C. If the sum of two angles in a linear pair is 180, then they are angles; Converse is not true and the definition does not pass.
    D. If each of the measures of two angles is 180, then the angles form a linear pair; Converse is true and the definition passes.
    E. If the sum of the measures of two angles is 180, then the angles form a linear pair; Converse is not true and the definition does not pass.

8. Parallel lines are lines that lie in the same plane and never intersect.
(26)

    A. Lines that lie in the same plane and never intersect are parallel lines; Converse is not true and the definition does not pass.

    B. Lines that never intersect are parallel lines; Converse is true and the definition passes.

    C. Parallel lines that never intersect lie in the same plane; Converse is not true and the definition does not pass.

    D. Lines that lie in the same plane and never intersect are parallel lines; Converse is true and the definition passes.

    E. Lines that lie in the same plane are parallel lines; Converse is true and the definition passes.

Identify each pair of angles below and decide whether the pair is congruent, supplementary, or neither.

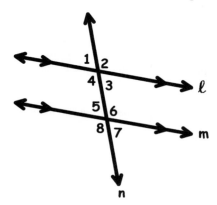

9. $\angle 3$ and $\angle 5$
(23)

    A. Alternate interior angles; congruent   B. Alternate exterior angles; congruent

    C. Adjacent angles; neither   D. Corresponding angles; congruent

    E. Alternate interior angles; supplementary

10. $\angle 2$ and $\angle 6$
(23)

    A. Alternate interior angles; congruent   B. Vertical angles; congruent

    C. Corresponding angles; congruent   D. Alternate exterior angles; neither

    E. Corresponding angles; supplementary

From each given statement below, select the definition, property, postulate, or theorem that justifies each prove statement.

11. Given: $\ell \parallel m$
(24)
    Prove: $\angle 3$ and $\angle 6$ are supplementary.

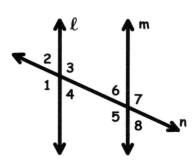

    A. If two parallel lines are cut by a transversal, then corresponding angles are supplementary.

    B. If two parallel lines are cut by a transversal, then alternate interior angles are supplementary.

    C. Definition of supplementary angles

    D. If two parallel lines are cut by a transversal, then interior angles on the same side of the transversal are supplementary.

    E. If two angles form a linear pair, then they are supplementary.

12. Given: ∠3 ≅ ∠5 (on the previous page)
(26) Prove: ℓ ∥ m

    A. Definition of parallel lines
    B. If two lines form congruent alternate interior angles with a transversal, then the lines are parallel.
    C. If two lines form congruent corresponding angles, then the lines are parallel.
    D. If two lines form supplementary interior angles on the same side of a transversal, then the lines are parallel.
    E. If two lines form congruent alternate exterior angles, then the lines are parallel.

13. Given: Lines m and n intersect (on the previous page).
(18) Prove: ∠5 ≅ ∠7

    A. Definition of congruent angles
    B. Pairs of vertical angles are congruent.
    C. If two parallel lines are cut by a transversal, then corresponding angles are congruent.
    D. If two parallel lines are cut by a transversal, then alternate interior angles are congruent.
    E. If two angles form a linear pair, then they are supplementary.

Complete each sentence below by selecting *always*, *sometimes*, or *never*.

14. Corresponding angles are _____ congruent.
(23)

    A. always   B. sometimes   C. never

15. If two parallel lines are cut by a transversal, interior angles on the same side of the transversal are
(24) _____ supplementary.

    A. always   B. sometimes   C. never

Given ℓ ∥ m , find the measure of each angle below.

16. ∠PTU
(24)

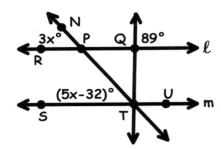

17. ∠QTP
(23)

Answer each question below.

18. ∠W and ∠Y are supplementary. If $m\angle W = 5x + 20$ and $m\angle Y = 4x - 11$, find $m\angle W$ and $m\angle Y$.
(16)

19. One angle of a linear pair is 10 more than two-thirds the other angle. Find the measure of *both* angles.
(17)

20. The difference between the measures of two complementary angles is 14. Find the measure of *both* angles.
(15)

Tell whether the arguments below are valid or invalid deductions.

21. If the two angles in a linear pair are equal, then each is a right angle. $\angle A$ and $\angle B$ are not right angles.
(2) Therefore, they are not an equal linear pair.

22. Parallel lines are lines that are coplanar and never intersect. Lines ℓ and m never intersect. Therefore, $\ell \parallel m$.
(2)

Do each proof below.

23. Given: $\angle Q \cong \angle S$, $\overline{PQ} \parallel \overline{RS}$
  Prove: $\overline{QR} \parallel \overline{ST}$

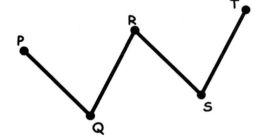

24. Given: $\overline{BC} \parallel \overline{AD}$, $\overline{AB} \parallel \overline{CD}$
  Prove: $m\angle BCD = m\angle DAB$

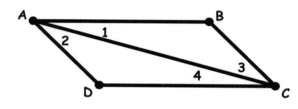

Chapter 5 Test

Tell whether each sentence below is true or false.

1. An exterior angle of a triangle (or any polygon) is complementary to its adjacent interior angle.
(31)

2. If triangles have two angles and one side congruent but the side is not between the angles, then the triangles
(34) are not necessarily congruent.

Complete each sentence below with the best of the choices given.

3. A scalene triangle has _____ congruent (equal) sides.
(29)

    A. no   B. two   C. three

4. A(n) _____ triangle has at least two congruent (equal) sides.
(29)

    A. scalene   B. acute   C. isosceles
    D. obtuse   E. right

5. The acute angles of a right triangle are _____.
(30)

    A. complementary   B. congruent   C. unique
    D. supplementary   E. a linear pair

6. The measure of an exterior angle of a triangle is _____ the sum of the measures of the
(31) _____ remote interior angles.

    A. equal to; largest   B. supplementary to; largest   C. complementary to; two
    D. complementary to; smallest   E. equal to; two

Answer question 7 based on the diagram below.

7. What kind of triangle is $\triangle FGH$ with respect to its sides? What kind of triangle is it with respect to its angles?
(29)

    A. Isosceles; obtuse   B. Scalene; obtuse   C. Isosceles; right
    D. Scalene; acute   E. Equilateral; acute

Find the measures of the angles of the triangle described below.

8. A triangle whose angles have measures x, $x+30$, and $x-30$. What kind of triangle is it with respect to its
(30) angles?

    A. 45, 75, 15; acute   B. 90, 120, 60; obtuse   C. 60, 90, 30; right
    D. 45, 90, 45; right   E. 60, 60, 60; acute

From each given statement below, select the definition, property, postulate, or theorem that justifies each prove statement.

9. Given: $\triangle SUV$ (above), $m\angle S = 15$, and $m\angle U = 50$
(30) Prove: $m\angle SVU = 115$

    A. The sum of the measures of the angles of a triangle is 180.
    B. Definition of supplementary angles
    C. The measure of the exterior angle of a triangle is equal to the sum of the measures of the two remote interior angles.
    D. The acute angles of a right triangle are complementary.
    E. If two of the angles in a triangle are small, the third one has to be big.

10. Given: $\triangle SUV$ and $\overrightarrow{ST}$ (above)
(31) Prove: $m\angle UVT = m\angle S + m\angle U$

    A. Addition Property
    B. The sum of the measures of the angles of a triangle is 180.
    C. Definition of supplementary angles
    D. The measure of the exterior angle of a triangle is equal to the sum of the measures of the two remote interior angles.
    E. Betweenness of Rays

Complete each sentence below by selecting *always*, *sometimes*, or *never*.

11. If a triangle is equilateral, then it is _____ isosceles.
(29)

    A. always   B. sometimes   C. never

12. An acute triangle _____ has an angle that is greater than 90°.
(29)

    A. always   B. sometimes   C. never

Given $\triangle BCD \cong \triangle CBE$ in the diagram below, fill in each of the blanks.

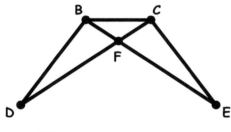

13. $\overline{BC} \cong$ _____ $\overline{BE} \cong$ _____ $\angle DBC \cong$ _____
(32)

Using the diagram, select the pair of lines that must be parallel if the statement below is true. If there are no lines that have to be parallel, select "none."

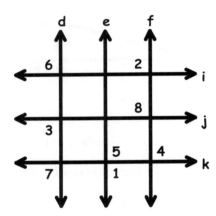

14. $\angle 4 \cong \angle 7$
(27)

   A. $k \parallel j$

   B. $d \parallel e$

   C. $k \parallel i$

   D. $d \parallel f$

   E. None

Answer each question below.

15. In $\triangle ABC$, the exterior angle adjacent to $\angle C$ has a measure of 120. If $m\angle A = 2x$ and $m\angle B = x + 15$, find
(31)

the measures of the angles of $\triangle ABC$.

16. If $\triangle JKL \cong \triangle QRS$, select the choice containing all of the congruent sides from the two triangles.
(32)

   A. $\overline{JK} \cong \overline{RS}$, $\overline{KL} \cong \overline{QS}$, $\overline{JL} \cong \overline{QR}$ B. $\overline{JK} \cong \overline{QR}$, $\overline{KL} \cong \overline{RS}$, $\overline{JL} \cong \overline{QS}$

   C. $\overline{JK} \cong \overline{RS}$, $\overline{KL} \cong \overline{QR}$, $\overline{JL} \cong \overline{QS}$ D. $\overline{JK} \cong \overline{QR}$, $\overline{KL} \cong \overline{QS}$, $\overline{JL} \cong \overline{RS}$

   E. $\overline{JK} \cong \overline{QS}$, $\overline{KL} \cong \overline{RS}$, $\overline{JL} \cong \overline{QR}$

17. Find x and y.
(30)

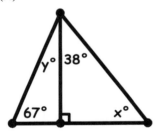

18. Find y.
(30)

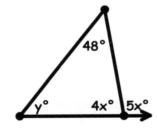

19. Find x.
(30)

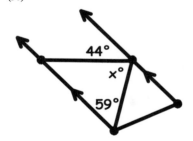

20. Find x and y.
(31)

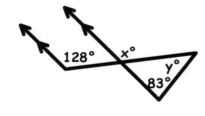

Select the converse of each statement below, and determine whether it is true or false.

21. If two triangles are congruent, then all three pairs of their sides are congruent.
(32)
    A. If all three pairs of the sides of two triangles are congruent, then the triangles are congruent; true
    B. If three sides of a triangle are congruent, then it is a triangle; false
    C. If all three pairs of the sides of two triangles are congruent, then the triangles are congruent; false
    D. If all three pairs of angles of two triangles are congruent, then the triangles are congruent; true
    E. If any three parts of two triangles are congruent, then the triangles are congruent; true

22. If a triangle is a right triangle, then it has two acute angles.
(29)
    A. If a triangle has one acute angle, then it is a right triangle; false
    B. If a triangle has one right angle, then it is a right triangle; false
    C. If a triangle has two acute angles, then it is a right triangle; true
    D. If a triangle has two acute angles, then it is a right triangle; false
    E. If a triangle has one right angle, then it is a right triangle; true

Do each proof below.

23. Given: $\overline{JK} \perp \overline{KL}$, $\overline{JM} \perp \overline{ML}$, $\angle KJL \cong \angle MJL$
    Prove: $\triangle JKL \cong \triangle JML$

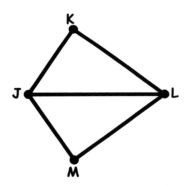

24. Given: $\overline{AF} \perp \overline{BD}$, $\overline{CE} \perp \overline{BD}$, $AB = CD$, $BE = FD$
    Prove: $\triangle ABF \cong \triangle CDE$

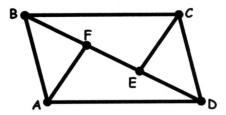

Chapter 6 Test

Tell whether each sentence below is true or false.

1. The Converse of the Base Angles Theorem can be used to prove that a triangle is isosceles.
(43)

2. C.P.C.T.C. is a shortcut for proving that two triangles are congruent.
(38)

Complete each sentence below with the best of the choices given.

3. A(n) _____ of a triangle is a segment drawn from any vertex of the triangle perpendicular to the
(41) opposite side and extended outside the triangle if necessary.

    A. transversal   B. median   C. bisector
    D. altitude   E. divisor

4. The measure of an exterior angle of a triangle is equal to the _____ of the measures of the two
(31) _____ interior angles.

    A. product; remote   B. difference; adjacent   C. sum; remote
    D. difference; remote   E. sum; adjacent

5. According to the _____ shortcut, two triangles are congruent if all three of their corresponding
(36) sides are congruent.

    A. Angle-Angle-Side   B. Side-Angle-Side   C. Angle-Side-Angle
    D. Side-Side-Side   E. Hypotenuse-Leg

Select the answer to each question below based on the accompanying diagram.

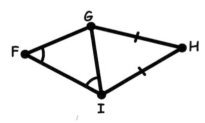

6. Which angles of $\triangle IGH$ are congruent?
(42)

    A. $\angle IGH$ and $\angle GIH$ B. $\angle IGH$ and $\angle GIF$ C. $\angle IGH$ and $\angle H$
    D. $\angle F$ and $\angle GIF$ E. $\angle H$ and $\angle GIH$

7. Which sides of $\triangle FGI$ are congruent?
(43)

    A. $\overline{FG}$ and $\overline{IG}$ B. $\overline{FG}$ and $\overline{FI}$ C. $\overline{FI}$ and $\overline{GH}$
    D. $\overline{FI}$ and $\overline{IG}$ E. $\overline{GH}$ and $\overline{HI}$

8. Select the triangle that shows the altitude of △*JKL* from vertex *J*.
(41)

A.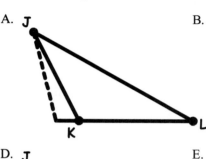

B.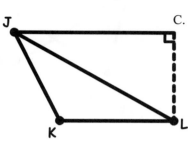

C.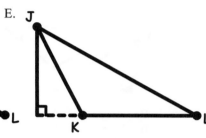

D.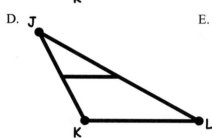

E.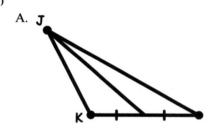

9. Select the triangle that shows the median of △*JKL* from vertex *K*.
(41)

A.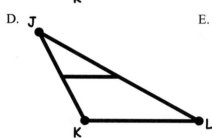

B.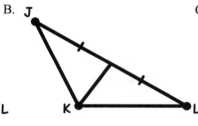

C.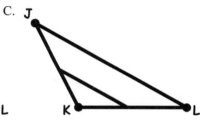

D.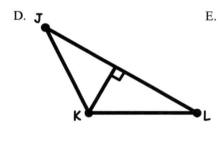

E.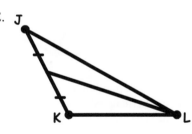

Select which shortcut can be used to prove each pair of triangles below congruent. If no method applies, choose "none."

10.
(35)

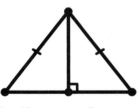

A. Side-Side-Side   B. Hypotenuse-Leg   C. Side-Angle-Side
D. Angle-Side-Angle   E. None

11.
(35)

A. Hypotenuse-Leg
D. Side-Angle-Side

B. Angle-Side-Angle
E. None

C. Side-Side-Side

12.
(34)

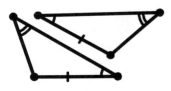

A. Side-Angle-Side
D. Hypotenuse-Leg

B. Angle-Side-Angle
E. None

C. Angle-Angle-Side

Find the measures of the angles of the triangle described below.

13. An isosceles triangle with a vertex angle of $88°$.
(42)

From each given statement below, select the definition, property, postulate, or theorem that justifies each prove statement.

14. Given: $\angle LIK \cong \angle IKJ$
(26) Prove: $\overline{LI} \parallel \overline{JK}$

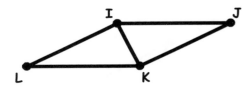

A. If two lines form congruent corresponding angles with a transversal, then the lines are parallel.
B. If two lines form congruent alternate exterior angles with a transversal, then the lines are parallel.
C. If two lines form congruent vertical angles with a transversal, then the lines are parallel.
D. If two lines form congruent alternate interior angles with a transversal, then the lines are parallel.
E. If two lines form congruent interior angles on the same side of a transversal, then the lines are parallel.

15. Given: $\triangle PQR$ and $\angle P \cong \angle Q$
(43) Prove: $\overline{PR} \cong \overline{RQ}$

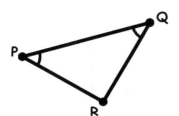

A. Converse of the Base Angles Theorem
B. All three sides of an equilateral triangle are congruent.
C. Angle-Angle-Side
D. Corresponding Parts of Congruent Triangles Are Congruent (C.P.C.T.C.)
E. Base Angles Theorem

Answer each question below.

16. Find *x*.
(30)

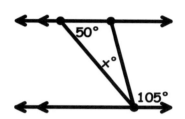

17. Find *x* and *y*.
(31)

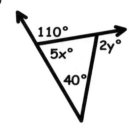

18. Find *x* and *y*.
(24)

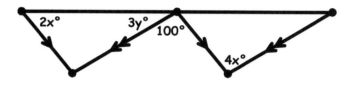

19. An angle is equal to one-third its complement. Find the angle's measure.
(15)

20. Two angles are a linear pair. The measure of the first angle minus 39 is equal to twice the measure of the
(17) second angle. What are the measures of *both* angles?

Select the converse of the statement below and determine whether it is true or false.

21. If a triangle is obtuse, then it has one angle that is greater than 90°.
(29)

    A. If a triangle has two angles that are greater than 90°, then it is obtuse; false

    B. If a triangle has one angle that is greater than 90°, then it is obtuse; true

    C. If a triangle has one angle that is greater than 90°, then it is obtuse; false

    D. If an angle is greater than 90°, then it is obtuse; false

    E. If a triangle has two angles that are greater than 90°, then it is obtuse; true

22. If two angles of a triangle are congruent (equal), then the sides opposite those angles are congruent (equal).
(43)

    A. If two opposite sides of a triangle are congruent (equal), then the angles of the triangle are congruent (equal); true

    B. If two sides of a triangle are congruent (equal), then the angles opposite those sides are congruent (equal); false

    C. If two sides of a triangle are congruent (equal), then the angles between those sides are congruent (equal); false

    D. If two opposite sides of a triangle are congruent (equal), then the angles of the triangle are congruent (equal); false

    E. If two sides of a triangle are congruent (equal), then the angles opposite those sides are congruent (equal); true

Do each proof below.

23. Given: $\overline{KM} \parallel \overline{JH}$, $\overline{KM} \cong \overline{JH}$, $\overline{JK} \cong \overline{KL}$
    Prove: $\overline{HK} \parallel \overline{ML}$

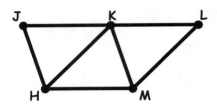

24. Given: $\triangle ABC$; $\overline{CA} \cong \overline{CB}$; $\overline{AD}$ and $\overline{BE}$ are altitudes of $\triangle ABC$.
    Prove: $\overline{AD} \cong \overline{BE}$

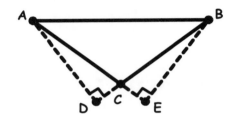

Chapter 7 Test

Tell whether each sentence below is true or false.

1.
(45) The sum of the lengths of any two sides of a triangle must be less than the length of the remaining side.

2.
(48) A statement is always logically equivalent to its contrapositive.

Complete each sentence below with the best of the choices given.

3. When _____ or _____ both sides of an inequality by a negative number, the inequality
(44) symbol must be flipped.

    A. adding; multiplying   B. adding; subtracting   C. subtracting; multiplying
    D. multiplying; dividing   E. subtracting; dividing

4. If the original statement is in the form "If a, then b," then the converse is in the form "_____."
(48)

    A. If b, then a B. If not b, then a C. If not b, then not a
    D. If not a, then b E. If not a, then not b

5. If the original statement is in the form "If a, then b," then the contrapositive is in the form
(48) "_____."

    A. If b, then a B. If not b, then a C. If not b, then not a
    D. If not a, then b E. If not a, then not b

6. If the original statement is in the form "If a, then b," then the inverse is in the form "_____."
(48)

    A. If b, then a B. If not b, then a C. If not b, then not a
    D. If not a, then b E. If not a, then not b

Tell whether each set of numbers below can represent the side lengths of a triangle.

7. **a.** 5, 8, 14   **b.** 12, 16, 20
(45)

Each question below lists the lengths of two sides of a triangle. For each question, tell what length the third side must be greater than and less than.

8. **a.** 7, 2   **b.** 12, 21
(45)

Select the choice that follows the correct sequence of steps in solving each inequality below.

9. $6x + 23 > -2x + 7$
(44)

    A. **(1)** $8x + 23 > 7$ (Subtraction Property of Inequality)
        (2) $8x > -16$ (Multiplication Property of Inequality)
        (3) $x > -2$ (Addition Property of Inequality)

B. **(1)** $8x + 23 > 7$ (Addition Property of Inequality)
(2) $8x > -16$ (Subtraction Property of Inequality)
(3) $x > -2$ (Addition Property of Inequality)

C. **(1)** $8x + 23 > 7$ (Addition Property of Inequality)
(2) $8x > -16$ (Subtraction Property of Inequality)
(3) $x > -2$ (Division Property of Inequality)

D. **(1)** $8x + 23 > 7$ (Multiplication Property of Inequality)
(2) $8x > -16$ (Division Property of Inequality)
(3) $x > -2$ (Subtraction Property of Inequality)

E. **(1)** $8x + 23 > 7$ (Division Property of Inequality)
(2) $8x > -16$ (Multiplication Property of Inequality)
(3) $x > -2$ (Division Property of Inequality)

10. $-\dfrac{1}{2}y - 1 \le 3$
(44)

A. **(1)** $-\dfrac{1}{2}y \le 4$ (Multiplication Property of Inequality)
(2) $y \ge -8$ (Multiplication Property of Inequality)

B. **(1)** $-\dfrac{1}{2}y \le 4$ (Addition Property of Inequality)
(2) $y \ge -8$ (Addition Property of Inequality)

C. **(1)** $-\dfrac{1}{2}y \le 4$ (Addition Property of Inequality)
(2) $y \ge -8$ (Multiplication Property of Inequality)

D. **(1)** $-\dfrac{1}{2}y \le 4$ (Division Property of Inequality)
(2) $y \ge -8$ (Addition Property of Inequality)

E. **(1)** $-\dfrac{1}{2}y \le 4$ (Multiplication Property of Inequality)
(2) $y \ge -8$ (Addition Property of Inequality)

Find the measures of the angles of each triangle described below.

11. An isosceles obtuse triangle with one angle that is 32°.
(30)

12. A right triangle where one of the two acute angles measures 8 times the other.
(30)

For each of the two true statements below, tell whether its converse, inverse, and contrapositive are also true.

13. If Mike lives in Honolulu, then he lives in Hawaii.
(48)

Converse: If Mike lives in Hawaii, then he lives in Honolulu. Is the converse true or false?

Inverse: If Mike does not live in Honolulu, then he does not live in Hawaii. Is the inverse true or false?

Contrapositive: If Mike does not live in Hawaii, then he does not live in Honolulu. Is the contrapositive true or false?

14. If two angles are both right angles, then they are congruent.
(48)

Converse: If two angles are congruent, then they are both right angles. Is the converse true or false?

Inverse: If two angles are not both right angles, then they are not congruent. Is the inverse true or false?

Contrapositive: If two angles are not congruent, then they are not both right angles. Is the contrapositive true or false?

From each given statement below, select the definition, property, postulate, or theorem that justifies each prove statement.

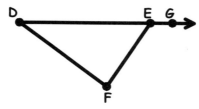

15. Given: $\triangle DEF$
(45) Prove: $EF + FD > DE$

    A. Exterior Angle Inequality Theorem   B. Addition Property of Inequality
    C. Whole Greater Than Its Part Property   D. Triangle Inequality Postulate
    E. If Unequal Angles, Then Unequal Sides

16. Given: $\triangle DEF$
(46) Prove: $\angle GEF > \angle F$

    A. Triangle Inequality Postulate   B. Exterior Angle Inequality Theorem
    C. Transitive Property of Inequality   D. Whole Greater Than Its Part Property
    E. If Unequal Sides, Then Unequal Angles

17. Given: $\angle DFE > \angle DEF$
(49) Prove: $DE > DF$

    A. Exterior Angle Inequality Theorem   B. If Unequal Angles, Then Unequal Sides
    C. Triangle Inequality Postulate   D. Whole Greater Than Its Part Property
    E. If Unequal Sides, Then Unequal Angles

Answer each question below based on the accompanying diagram.

18. In $\triangle IJK$, $IJ = 4$ and $JK = 6$. Is $\angle I$ or $\angle K$ greater?
(49)

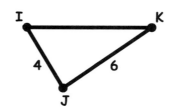

121

19. Find $m + n$.
(30)

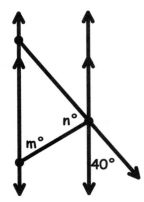

20. $\triangle MNO$ is equilateral. Find x and y.
(30)

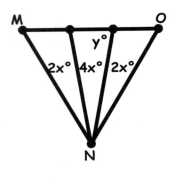

21. Find x.
(42)

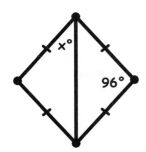

22. Find a.
(31)

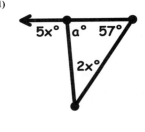

Do each proof below. Use the indirect method on 24.

23. Given: $\overline{PQ} \cong \overline{PR}$, $\overline{QR} \parallel \overline{ST}$
Prove: $\triangle SPT$ is isosceles.

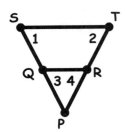

24. Given: $IJ = KJ$
(47)
Prove: $IL \neq LM$

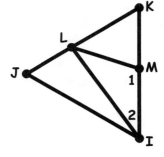

Chapter 8 Test

Tell whether each sentence below is true or false.

1.
(52)   Consecutive pairs of angles of a parallelogram are congruent.

2.
(53)   If both pairs of opposite sides are congruent, then a quadrilateral is a parallelogram.

Complete each sentence below with the best of the choices given.

3.
(50)   The sum of the measures of the angles of any quadrilateral is _____.

    A. 180   B. 720   C. 360
    D. 90   E. never the same

4.
(51)   A _____ is a quadrilateral that has only one pair of opposite sides parallel.

    A. rhombus   B. parallelogram   C. rectangle
    D. square   E. trapezoid

5.
(53)   The _____ of a parallelogram bisect each other.

    A. altitudes   B. legs   C. medians
    D. divisor lines   E. diagonals

6.
(55)   The line segment joining the midpoints of two sides of a triangle is _____ to the third side and _____ its length.

    A. perpendicular; equal to   B. parallel; equal to   C. parallel; one-half
    D. perpendicular; one-half   E. parallel; twice

Select which type of polygon each figure below is.

7.
(52)

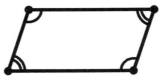

    A. square   B. parallelogram   C. rectangle
    D. rhombus   E. trapezoid

8.
(51)

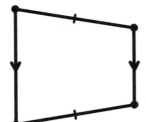

    A. isosceles trapezoid   B. parallelogram   C. rhombus
    D. square   E. triangle

9.
(56)

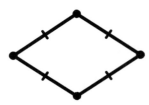

    A. trapezoid   B. isosceles trapezoid   C. square
    D. rhombus   E. rectangle

Complete each sentence below by selecting *always*, *sometimes*, or *never*.

10. A rhombus is _____ a parallelogram.
(56)
    A. always   B. sometimes   C. never

11. Pairs of consecutive angles of a parallelogram are _____ congruent.
(52)
    A. always   B. sometimes   C. never

For each of the two true statements below, tell whether its converse, inverse, and contrapositive are also true.

12. If a figure is a rhombus, then it is a parallelogram.
(56)

Converse: If a figure is a parallelogram, then it is a rhombus. Is the converse true or false?

Inverse: If a figure is not a rhombus, then it is not a parallelogram. Is the inverse true or false?

Contrapositive: If a figure is not a parallelogram, then it is not a rhombus. Is the contrapositive true or false?

13. If a figure is not a rectangle, then it is not a square.
(56)

Converse: If a figure is not a square, then it is not a rectangle. Is the converse true or false?

Inverse: If a figure is a rectangle, then it is a square. Is the inverse true or false?

Contrapositive: If a figure is a square, then it is a rectangle. Is the contrapositive true or false?

From each given statement below, select the definition, property, postulate, or theorem that justifies each prove statement.

14. Given: Rhombus *RSTU*
(57)   Prove: $\overline{RT} \perp \overline{SU}$

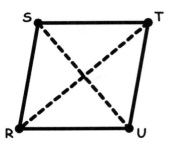

    A. The diagonals of a rhombus bisect each other.
    B. Definition of a rhombus
    C. Definition of perpendicular lines
    D. The medians of a rhombus are perpendicular to each other.
    E. The diagonals of a rhombus are perpendicular to each other.

15. Given: Isosceles trapezoid *MNOP*
(51) Prove: $\overline{MO} \cong \overline{PN}$

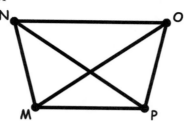

   A. The diagonals of an isosceles trapezoid are perpendicular to each other.
   B. The diagonals of an isosceles trapezoid are congruent.
   C. Definition of an isosceles trapezoid
   D. Hypotenuse-Leg
   E. The altitudes of an isosceles trapezoid are congruent.

16. Given: Quadrilateral *IJKL*, $\overline{IJ} \parallel \overline{LK}$, $\overline{IJ} \cong \overline{LK}$
(55) Prove: *IJKL* is a parallelogram.

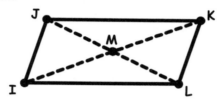

   A. If one pair of opposite sides is both parallel and congruent, then a quadrilateral is a parallelogram.
   B. If the diagonals bisect each other, then a quadrilateral is a parallelogram.
   C. If both pairs of opposite sides are parallel, then a quadrilateral is a parallelogram.
   D. If the diagonals are congruent, then a quadrilateral is a parallelogram.
   E. If both pairs of opposite sides are congruent, then a quadrilateral is a parallelogram.

Answer each question below.

17. Find *x*, *y*, and *z*.
(51)

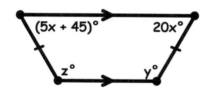

18. Find *x*.
(55)

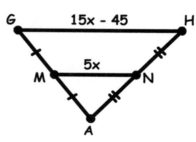

19. Find *y*.
(50)

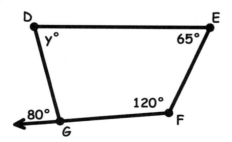

20. In parallelogram *RSWY*, find $m\angle R$ and $m\angle S$.
(52)

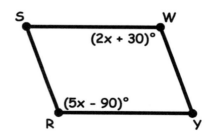

21. In $\triangle FGH$, $FG = 8.7$, $FH = 4.5$ and $GH = 6.1$. Which is the smallest angle of the triangle?
(49)

22. In $\triangle JKL$, $m\angle J = 40$ and $m\angle L$ is 3 times $m\angle K$. Find $m\angle K$ and $m\angle L$.
(30)

Do each proof below.

23. Given: Rectangle $EJHG$, $\overline{JI} \cong \overline{FG}$

Prove: $\overline{EI} \cong \overline{HF}$

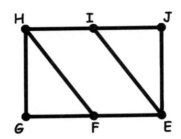

24. Given: $\triangle NOP \cong \triangle QRP$; N is the midpoint of $\overline{MO}$.

Prove: $MNQR$ is a parallelogram.

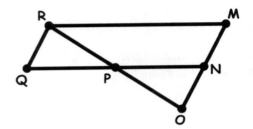

126

Chapter 9 Test

Tell whether each sentence below is true or false.

1.
(58)
The number of angles of a polygon is equal to the number of its sides.

2.
(61)
A regular polygon is a convex polygon where every one of its sides is congruent and every one of its interior angles is congruent.

Complete each sentence below with the best of the choices given.

3.
(58)
A five-sided polygon is called a _____, and a six-sided polygon is called a _____.

    A. pentagon; hexagon   B. quadrilateral; pentagon   C. hexagon; pentagon

    D. pentagon; heptagon   E. nonagon; hexagon

4.
(61)
The measure of each exterior angle of a regular polygon equals _____.

    A. $180n$ B. 360 – the measure of each interior angle

    C. $\dfrac{180(n-2)}{n}$ D. 180 – the measure of each interior angle

    E. $\dfrac{180n}{n-2}$

5.
(59)
The sum of the measures of the interior angles of a polygon with n sides is _____.

    A. $\dfrac{360}{n}$ B. $180(n-2)$ C. $360n$

    D. $\dfrac{180(n-2)}{n}$ E. $180n$

Select which type of polygon each figure below is and tell whether it's convex or concave.

6.
(58)

    A. hexagon; concave   B. heptagon; convex   C. pentagon; concave

    D. pentagon; convex   E. hexagon; convex

7.
(58)

   A. quadrilateral; convex   B. pentagon; concave   C. hexagon; concave
   D. pentagon; convex   E. hexagon; convex

8.
(58)

   A. decagon; convex   B. octagon; convex   C. octagon; concave
   D. nonagon; concave   E. nonagon; convex

For each problem below, select the choice which shows all of the diagonals in the polygon and tells how many there are.

9.
(58)

A.

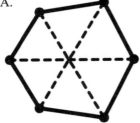

3 diagonals

B.

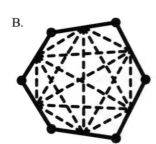

15 diagonals

C.

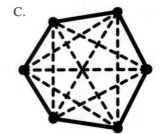

10 diagonals

D.

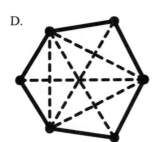

6 diagonals

E.

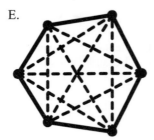

9 diagonals

10.
(58)

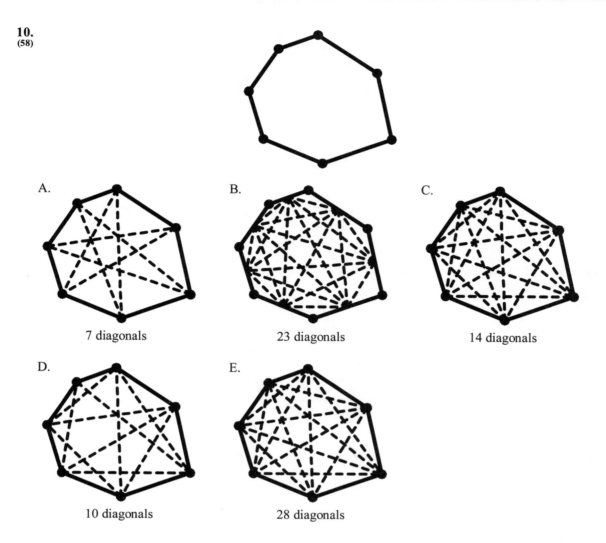

A.

7 diagonals

B.

23 diagonals

C.

14 diagonals

D.

10 diagonals

E.

28 diagonals

Determine which type of regular polygon each figure below is and then find the measures of the indicated interior and exterior angles.

11.
(61)

A. regular hexagon; interior: 120; exterior: 60
C. regular octagon; interior: 135; exterior: 45
E. regular heptagon; interior: 129; exterior: 51

B. regular hexagon; interior: 129; exterior: 51
D. regular heptagon; interior: 120; exterior: 60

12.
(61)

A. regular octagon; interior: 135; exterior: 45   B. regular octagon; interior: 140; exterior: 40
C. regular decagon; interior: 140; exterior: 40   D. regular decagon; interior: 144; exterior: 36
E. regular nonagon; interior: 144; exterior: 36

Find the sum of the measures of the exterior angles of the polygon below.

13.
(60)

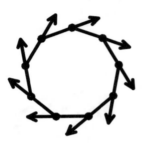

Complete each sentence below by selecting *always*, *sometimes*, or *never*.

14. A regular polygon is _____ convex.
(61)

A. always   B. sometimes   C. never

15. The sum of the measures of all the exterior angles of a polygon is _____ equal to 180.
(60)

A. always   B. sometimes   C. never

Answer the question below.

16. Read the following true statement and then tell whether its converse, inverse, and contrapositive are also true.
(61)

   If a figure is a regular polygon, then it is equilateral.

Converse: If a figure is equilateral, then it is a regular polygon. Is the converse true or false?

Inverse: If a figure is not a regular polygon, then it is not equilateral. Is the inverse true or false?

Contrapositive: If a figure is not equilateral, then it is not a regular polygon. Is the contrapositive true or false?

Find the perimeter of each polygon described below.

17. A rectangle with length measuring 14 and width measuring 3.
(62)

130

18. A regular nonagon with sides measuring 14.
(62)

Answer each question below.

19. Find $x + y$.
(50)

110°
y°
x°
80°

20. Find x.
(59)

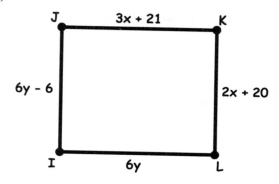

115°
x°
110°
x°
(x + 25)°
(x – 30)°

21. Find $a + b + c + d$.
(30)

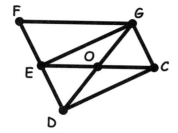

c° d°
a° b°
65°

22. In rectangle *IJKL*, find x and y.
(56)

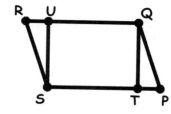

J   3x + 21   K
6y – 6   2x + 20
I   6y   L

Do each proof below.

23. Given: *GCDE* is a rectangle;
        GCEF is a parallelogram.
    Prove: $\triangle GDF$ is isosceles.

F   G
   O
E   C
   D

24. Given: *PQRS* is a parallelogram;
        $\overline{TQ} \perp \overline{QR}$; $\overline{US} \perp \overline{PS}$.
    Prove: $\triangle QTP \cong \triangle SUR$

R U   Q
S   T P

131

Chapter 10 Test

Tell whether each sentence below is true or false.

1. If $\triangle FGH \sim \triangle QRS$, then $\dfrac{SQ}{HF} = \dfrac{RS}{GH}$.
(65)

2. If one angle and one side of a triangle are congruent to a corresponding angle and side of another triangle,
(69) then the triangles are similar.

Complete each sentence below with the best of the choices given.

3. A _____ is two ratios that are set equal to each other.
(64)

    A. cross-multiplication   B. transversal   C. geometric mean
    D. proportion   E. similarity

4. If a line is _____ to one side of a triangle and intersects the other two sides, then the line divides
(67) those sides proportionally.

    A. perpendicular   B. congruent   C. parallel
    D. a median   E. an altitude

5. If two triangles are _____, then their vertices can be paired in a correspondence so that all pairs of
(70) corresponding angles are congruent and all pairs of corresponding sides are proportional.

    A. isosceles   B. intersecting   C. acute
    D. adjacent   E. similar

Tell whether each pair of ratios below is equal.

6. **a.** $\dfrac{4}{9}, \dfrac{20}{45}$ **b.** $63:27$, $14:6$ **c.** 11 to 44, 44 to 11
(63)

Answer each question below.

7. Solve for r in $\dfrac{r}{r+15} = \dfrac{3}{8}$ by cross-multiplying.
(64)

8. Find the geometric mean of 2 and 32.
(64)

In the triangle below, find each of the ratios indicated, and make sure your answers are fully reduced. Do the ratios show that the sides are divided proportionally?

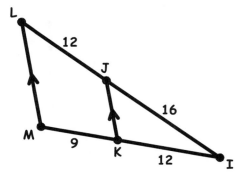

9.
(67)
$\dfrac{IL}{JL}$ and $\dfrac{IM}{KM}$

Write a proportion to represent each question below; then solve the proportion to get your answer.

10. The garage on a house blueprint measures 4 inches wide and 6 inches long. If the actual garage is going to
(64) have a length of 45 feet, what will its width be?

11. The ratio of the corresponding sides of two similar quadrilaterals is $7:4$. If the length of the longest side of
(64) the larger quadrilateral is 56 cm, find the length of the longest side of the smaller quadrilateral.

From each given statement below, select the definition, property, postulate, or theorem that justifies each prove statement.

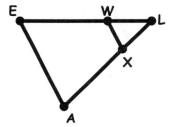

12. Given: $\dfrac{WL}{EL} = \dfrac{XL}{AL} = \dfrac{XW}{AE}$
(69)
Prove: $\triangle AEL \sim \triangle XWL$

    A. Triangle Inequality Postulate   B. Converse of the definition of similar triangles
    C. Side-Angle-Side Similarity   D. Side-Side-Side Similarity
    E. Hypotenuse-Leg

13. Given $\triangle ELA \sim \triangle WLX$
(70)
    Prove: $\dfrac{EL}{WL} = \dfrac{AL}{XL}$

    A. Converse of the definition of similar triangles   B. Angle-Angle Similarity
    C. Side-Side-Side Similarity   D. Side-Angle-Side Similarity
    E. Triangle Inequality Postulate

133

Use proportions to tell whether the pair of figures below are similar or not similar.

14.
(65)

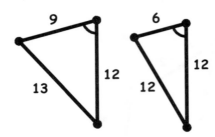

Select which shortcut can be used to prove that each pair of triangles below are similar. If no method applies, select "none."

15.
(69)

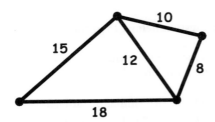

A. Angle-Angle Similarity   B. Hypotenuse-Leg   C. Side-Angle-Side Similarity
D. Side-Side-Side Similarity   E. None

16.
(68)

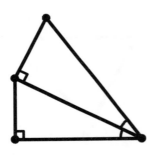

A. Angle-Angle Similarity   B. Side-Side-Side Similarity   C. Side-Angle-Side Similarity
D. Hypotenuse-Leg   E. None

17.
(69)

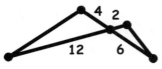

A. Hypotenuse-Leg   B. Angle-Angle Similarity   C. Side-Angle-Side Similarity
D. Side-Side-Side Similarity   E. None

Chapter 11 Test

Tell whether each sentence below is true or false.

1.
(73) According to the Pythagorean Theorem, in any right triangle the squares of the two legs added together equals the square of the hypotenuse.

2.
(79) The cosine ratio for a particular angle in a right triangle is the opposite side to that angle divided by the hypotenuse.

Complete each sentence below with the best of the choices given.

3.
(78) The tangent ratio for a particular angle in a right triangle is the _____ to that angle divided by the _____ .

 A. opposite side; adjacent side   B. opposite side; hypotenuse   C. adjacent side; hypotenuse
 D. adjacent side; opposite side   E. hypotenuse; opposite side

4.
(72) The altitude to the hypotenuse of a right triangle forms two triangles that are _____ to each other and to the original triangle.

 A. identical   B. unrelated   C. congruent
 D. adjacent   E. similar

5.
(74) A(n) _____ is three whole numbers that can be the side lengths of a right triangle.

 A. Pythagorean Triple   B. ordered triple   C. Pythagorean Set
 D. triangle set   E. irrational triple

Simplify each irrational number below; then estimate it to two decimal places.

6. $\sqrt{75}$
(74)

7. $\sqrt{128}$
(74)

Tell whether each set of numbers below is a Pythagorean Triple.

8. $\{15, 20, 25\}$
(74)

9. $\{6, 9, 12\}$
(74)

Find the missing lengths in the right triangles below.

10. Find x.
(74)

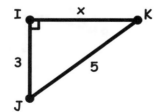

11. Find x.
(74)

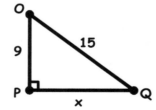

Use proportions or the Pythagorean Theorem to find the missing values below. If needed, estimate your answer to two decimal places.

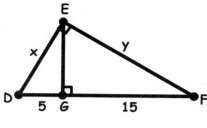

12. Find x.
(72)

13. Find y.
(72)

Calculate each trigonometric ratio below. Estimate your answers to two decimal places.

14. $\tan 25°$
(78)

15. $\sin 65°$
(79)

Use the tangent ratio to find the missing leg of each right triangle below. Estimate your answers to two decimal places.

16.
(78)

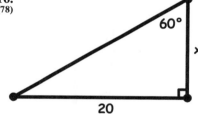

17.
(78)

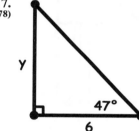

Answer each question below.

18. A basketball hoop is 10 feet high. If Steve is 5 feet tall and standing 12 feet away from the hoop, what is
(74) the distance from the top of Steve's head to the hoop?

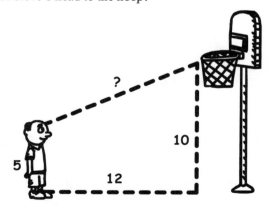

137

19. Find *x*.
(74)

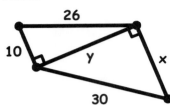

20. Find *y*.
(76)

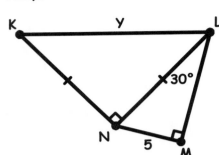

Write an equation to represent each question below; then solve the equation to get your answer.

21. Fiona is standing 26 meters from the base of
(78) an oak tree. If she measures the angle of
elevation to the top of the tree to be 37°, how
tall is the tree? Estimate your answer to two
decimal places.

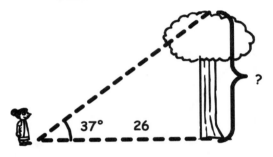

22. A plane veered off its course at an angle of
(79) 11°. If the plane ended up 170 miles due
west of its planned destination, how far did
it fly? Estimate your answer to two decimal
places.

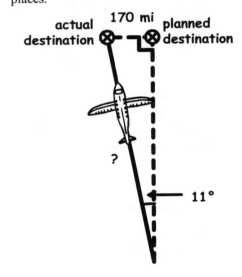

Do each proof below.

23. Given: $\triangle FCE \sim \triangle HID$; $\overline{GD}$ bisects $\angle IDF$.
Prove: $\triangle FCE \sim \triangle HCD$

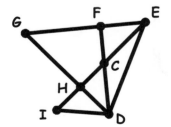

24. Given: *PCDE* is a parallelogram; $\overline{PF} \cong \overline{DG}$
Prove: *FCGE* is a parallelogram.

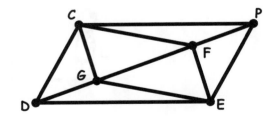

Chapter 12 Test

Tell whether each sentence below is true or false.

1. If a radius is drawn to the point of tangency of a tangent line, then the radius is perpendicular to the tangent
(83) line.

2. An inscribed angle is equal in measure to the measure of its intercepted arc.
(87)

Complete each sentence below with the best of the choices given.

3. A(n) _____ line is a line which intersects a circle in two different points.
(81)

    A. tangent   B. radial   C. secant
    D. cosine   E. inscribed

4. An inscribed angle that intercepts a _____ is a right angle.
(87)

    A. circle   B. minor arc   C. radius
    D. semicircle   E. chord

5. The measure of an angle formed by two chords (or secants) intersecting in the interior of a circle is equal to
(88) one-half the _____ of the measures of the two intercepted arcs.

    A. sum   B. difference   C. product
    D. quotient   E. square

Select whether each of the following parts of circle *O* is a radius, diameter, chord, tangent line, or secant line.

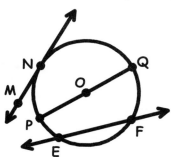

6. $\overleftrightarrow{EF}$
(81)

    A. radius   B. diameter   C. chord
    D. tangent line   E. secant line

7. $\overline{MN}$
(81)

    A. radius   B. diameter   C. chord
    D. tangent line   E. secant line

8. $\overline{QO}$
(81)

    A. radius   B. diameter   C. chord
    D. tangent line   E. secant line

Find the degree measure of each arc or central angle indicated below.

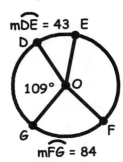

$m\overset{\frown}{DE} = 43$ E

D

109° O

G F

$m\overset{\frown}{FG} = 84$

9. ∠EOF
(84)

10. $\overset{\frown}{DGF}$
(84)

Calculate the linear measure of each arc indicated below. Give your answers in terms of π.

11. $\overset{\frown}{PQ}$
(85)

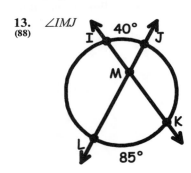

135°

O

12 Q

P

12. $\overset{\frown}{TSU}$
(85)

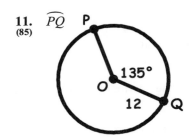

S O 80°

9

T

U

Find the degree measure of each angle below.

13. ∠IMJ
(88)

40°

I J

M

L K

85°

14. ∠DPR
(88)

E

D

P R $m\overset{\frown}{DR} = 26$ $m\overset{\frown}{ET} = 118$

T

Find each missing line segment indicated below.

15. Find *IM.*
(89)

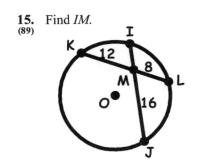

K

12

I

8

M L

O

16

J

16. Find *ST.*
(89)

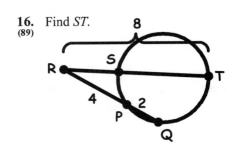

8

R S T

4 2

P

Q

140

Answer each question below.

17. Find *x*. Assume $\overline{SG}$ is tangent to circle *O*
(83) at point *S*.

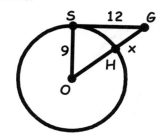

18. Find *y*.
(87)

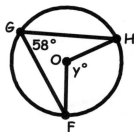

19. If $\overline{QR}$ is tangent to $\odot O$, find *x*.
(83)

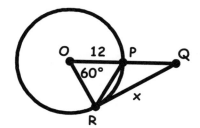

20. If $m\widehat{DE} = 50$, find *d*.
(84)

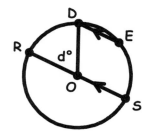

From each given statement below, select the definition, property, postulate, or theorem that justifies each prove statement.

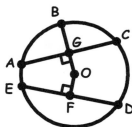

21. Given: $\overline{AC} \perp \overline{OB}$
(82) Prove: $\overline{AG} \cong \overline{GC}$

   A. If a line through the center of a circle is perpendicular to a chord, it also bisects the chord.
   B. When a radius intersects a chord, it also bisects the chord.
   C. Definition of a segment bisector
   D. If any line in a circle is perpendicular to a chord, it also bisects the chord.
   E. In the same circle, chords equidistant from the center of the circle are congruent.

22. Given: $\overline{OG} \cong \overline{OF}$
(82) Prove: $\overline{AC} \cong \overline{DE}$

   A. If a line through the center of a circle is perpendicular to a chord, it also bisects the chord.
   B. In the same circle, all chords are congruent.
   C. In the same circle, all radii are congruent.
   D. In the same circle, if any radii are perpendicular to two chords, then the chords are congruent.
   E. In the same circle, chords equidistant from the center of the circle are congruent.

Do each proof below.

23. Given: $\overline{IK}$ and $\overline{IM}$ are secant segments;
$IK = IM$
Prove: $IJ = IL$

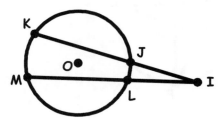

24. Given: $\overset{\frown}{RP} \cong \overset{\frown}{PS}$ in $\odot O$
Prove: $\overline{ST} \cong \overline{RT}$

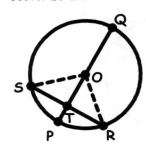

Chapter 13 Test

Tell whether each sentence below is true or false.

1.
(91) The area of a parallelogram is equal to one-half the product of the base and the altitude.

2.
(94) A segment of a circle is a region of a circle bounded by a chord and the minor arc that it intercepts.

Complete each sentence below with the best of the choices given.

3.
(92) The area of a rhombus is equal to one-half the product of _____.

    A. any two sides   B. any side and an altitude   C. two altitudes
    D. the two diagonals   E. an altitude and a median

4.
(94) If two polygons are similar, then the ratio of their areas is equal to the _____ of the ratio of the lengths of any two corresponding sides.

    A. square root   B. sum   C. inverse
    D. square   E. product

5.
(91) The area of a(n) _____ is equal to one-half the product of the base and the altitude.

    A. trapezoid   B. triangle   C. rhombus
    D. parallelogram   E. isosceles trapezoid

Calculate the area of each rectangle described below.

6.
(90) A rectangle with a base of 15 inches and an altitude of 7 inches.

7.
(90) A rectangle with an altitude of 30 cm and a diagonal of 50 cm.

Calculate the area of each figure below.

8. $\triangle PQR$
(91)

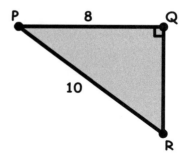

9. $\triangle IJK$
(91)

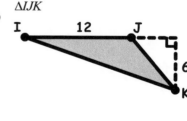

10. □*MNOP*
(91)

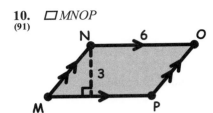

11.
(91)

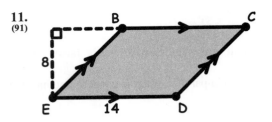

12.
(92)

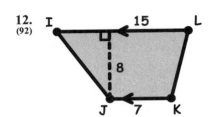

13. *PR* = 6 and *QS* = 4
(92)

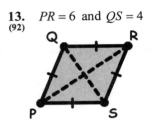

14.
(91)

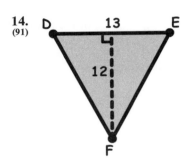

15. △*QRS*
(91)

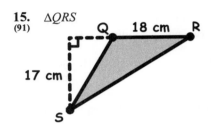

16. Regular pentagon *IJKLM*
(93)

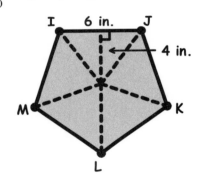

17. □*WXYZ*
(91)

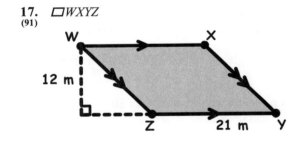

18. Trapezoid *BCDE*
(92)

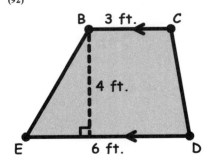

Calculate the area of each shaded region below. Give your answers in terms of π.

19.
(94)

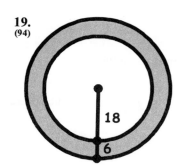

20.
(94)

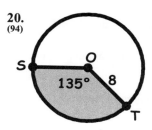

Write an equation to represent each question below; then solve the equation to get your answer.

21. In $\triangle TUV$, $\angle T$ is a right angle, $TU = 10$, $UV = 26$, and $VT = 24$. If $\triangle TUV \sim \triangle WXY$ and $WY = 72$, what
(94) is the area of $\triangle WXY$?

22. If the area of $PQRS = 60$, find x.
(92)

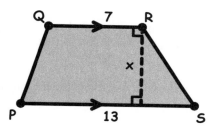

Do each proof below.

23. Given: $\overline{LK} \cong \overline{IJ}$
Prove: $\overline{LJ} \cong \overline{IK}$

24. Given: $\overrightarrow{PR}$ is tangent to $\odot O$ at P;
$\overrightarrow{QR}$ is tangent to $\odot O$ at Q.

Prove: $\overrightarrow{RS}$ bisects $\angle PRQ$.

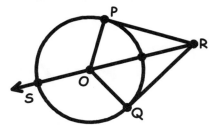

145

Chapter 14 Test

Tell whether each sentence below is true or false.

1.
(95) The total (surface) area of a rectangular solid is its length times its width times its altitude.

2.
(99) The volume and surface area of a sphere can both be calculated if you know only the radius of the sphere.

Complete each sentence below with the best of the choices given.

3.
(96) The volume of a prism equals the product of the _____ and the _____.

A. area of a lateral side; altitude
B. area of the base; slant height
C. perimeter of the base; area of a lateral side
D. perimeter of the base; altitude
E. area of the base; altitude

4.
(96) The total (surface) area of a prism is equal to the product of the _____ and the _____ of a base plus 2 times the _____.

A. altitude; perimeter; area of a lateral side
B. altitude; perimeter; area of a base
C. slant height; perimeter; altitude
D. slant height; perimeter; area of a base
E. altitude; area; area of a lateral side

5.
(98) The volume of a cone is equal to _____ times the area of the base times the altitude, but since the base is a circle, the formula is written as _____.

A. one-half; $V = \frac{1}{2}\pi r^2 a$
B. two; $V = 2\pi r^2 a$
C. one-third; $V = \frac{1}{3}\pi r^2 a$
D. two; $V = 2\pi ra$
E. one-third; $V = \frac{1}{3}\pi ra$

Calculate the area of each shaded region below. Give your answers in terms of π.

6.
(94)

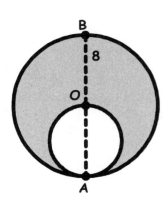

7.
(94)

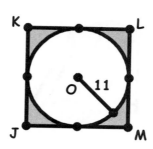

A. $484 - 121\pi$
D. 121π

B. 363π
E. $121\pi - 121$

C. $484\pi - 121$

8.
(94)

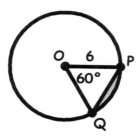

A. $36\pi - 6$
D. $6\pi - 9\sqrt{3}$

B. $6\pi - 6\sqrt{3}$
E. $6\pi - 6$

C. $36\pi - 9\sqrt{3}$

Calculate the surface area and volume of each rectangular solid below.

9.
(95)

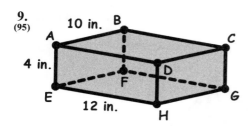

10.
(95)

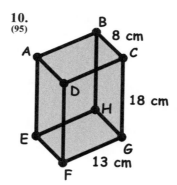

Select which type of solid each figure below is.

11.
(97)

A. rectangular pyramid
D. triangular pyramid

B. rectangular prism
E. triangular cone

C. triangular prism

12.
(96)

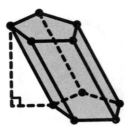

    A. oblique pentagonal prism   B. oblique hexagonal prism   C. oblique rectangular prism
    D. pentagonal pyramid   E. rectangular prism

Calculate the total (surface) area of each prism below.

13. Perimeter of base = 24; Area of base = 30
(96)

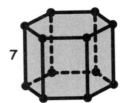

7

14. Base is a regular pentagon; Area of base = 50
(96)

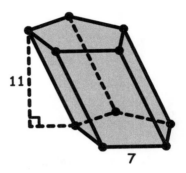

11

7

Calculate the total (surface) area of each solid below. If your answer uses π, give your answers in terms of π.

15. Sphere
(99)

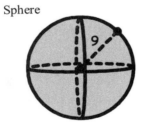

9

16. Base is a square.
(97)

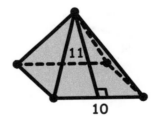

11

10

Calculate the volume of each solid below. If your answer uses π, give your answers in terms of π.

17. Area of base = 707
(96)

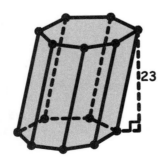

23

18.
(98)

9

27

148

19. Base is a regular pentagon of area 35. Altitude = 9.

(97)

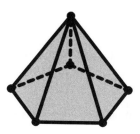

Answer each question below.

20. If the area of the sector is 40π, find n.

(94)

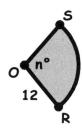

21. Find c.

(93)

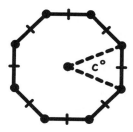

22. The edges of a large cube are 4 times as long as the edges of a smaller, similar cube. What is the ratio of the

(100) volume of the large cube to the volume of the small cube?

Do each proof below. Number 24 proves that an apothem of a regular polygon bisects a side of that polygon.

23. Given: $\overline{KL} \parallel \overline{IJ}$

Prove: $\widehat{IK} \cong \widehat{JL}$

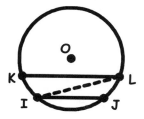

24. Given: $\overline{OP}$ is an apothem of regular polygon $JKLMN$.

Prove: $\overline{OP}$ bisects $\overline{KL}$.

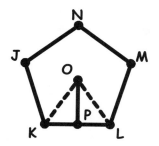

Chapter 15 Test

Tell whether each sentence below is true or false.

1.
(102)
The distance (d) between points (x_1, y_1) and (x_2, y_2) may be found with the formula $d = \sqrt{(x_2 + x_1)^2 + (y_2 + y_1)^2}$.

2.
(104)
The point-slope form of a linear equation is $y - y_0 = m(x - x_0)$, where m is the slope and (x_0, y_0) is any point on the line.

Complete each sentence below with the best of the choices given.

3.
(101)
Each point on a coordinate plane can be represented by a pair of numbers called the _____ and _____ of the point.

    A. *x*-coordinate; *y*-coordinate   B. origin; vertex
    C. origin; x-y coordinate   D. ordered pair; x-y coordinate
    E. ordered pair; quadrant

4.
(103)
If the slopes of two nonvertical lines are _____, then the lines are perpendicular.

    A. congruent   B. inverse square roots   C. inverse squares
    D. negative reciprocals   E. reciprocals

5.
(104)
The slope-intercept form of a linear equation is _____, where m is the _____ and b is the *y*-coordinate of the _____ of the line.

    A. $y = m(x + b)$; slope; *y*-intercept   B. $y = mx + b$; slope; origin
    C. $y - a = m(x - b)$; slope; *y*-intercept   D. $y = mx + b$; slope; *y*-intercept
    E. $y = mx + b$; *y*-intercept; slope

Find the missing coordinates of the points on each diagram below.

6.
(101)
Rectangle *EFGH*

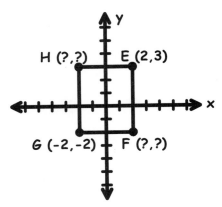

7.
(101)
Isosceles right triangle *OPQ*

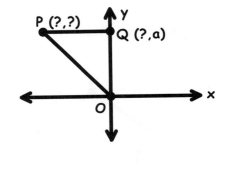

150

Calculate the area of each shaded region below. If your answer uses π, give your answers in terms of π.

8. $\overset{\frown}{JIK}$ is a semicircle.
(94)

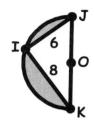

A. $10\pi - 24$ B. $12.5\pi - 14$
C. $12.5\pi - 24$ D. $25\pi - 24$
E. $25\pi - 14$

9. Parallelogram *ORST*
(102)

Find the midpoint of each line segment below.

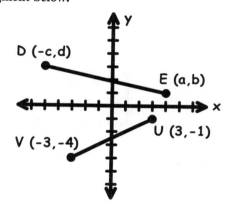

10. $\overline{DE}$
(102)

A. $\left(\dfrac{-a+c}{2}, \dfrac{-b-d}{2} \right)$

B. $\left(\dfrac{a+c}{4}, \dfrac{b+d}{4} \right)$

C. $\left(\dfrac{a-c}{2}, \dfrac{b-d}{2} \right)$

D. $(a-c, b-d)$

E. $\left(\dfrac{a-c}{2}, \dfrac{b+d}{2} \right)$

11. $\overline{UV}$
(102)

Find the lengths of the dashed sides of each diagram below.

12. Parallelogram *OWSD*
(102)

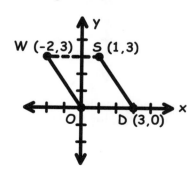

151

13. Right triangle OPQ
(102)

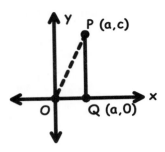

A. $\sqrt{a^2 - c^2}$

B. $\dfrac{a^2 + c^2}{2}$

C. $\sqrt{a^2 + c^2}$

D. $\sqrt{\dfrac{ac}{2}}$

E. $\sqrt{2a^2 + 2c^2}$

Answer each question below.

14. List the lines below in order of their slopes from least to greatest.
(103)

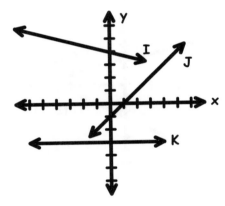

A. J, K, I
D. J, I, K

B. K, J, I
E. I, K, J

C. I, J, K

15. Calculate the slopes of lines E and F.
(103)

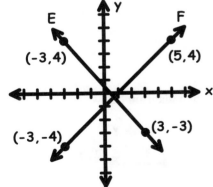

16. A right prism has an altitude of 16 cm and a base that is a right triangle with legs measuring 3 cm and 4 cm.
(100) Find the total (surface) area of a similar right prism that has a base whose legs measure 6 cm and 8 cm.

17.
(97) What is the volume of a right pyramid that has an altitude of 18 and a base which is a rhombus with diagonals measuring 10 and 24?

Select the equation for each line described below.

18.
(104) The line crossing the point $(-3,8)$ and with slope $=-1$.

    A. $y-3=-1(x+8)$
    B. $y-8=-1(x+3)$
    C. $y+8=-1(x-3)$

    D. $y=-x+3$
    E. $y=-x-8$

19.
(104) The line that crosses the point $(2,-5)$ and is perpendicular to the line $y=\dfrac{2}{3}x+4$.

    A. $y-5=\dfrac{2}{3}(x+2)$
    B. $y-2=\dfrac{3}{2}(x+5)$
    C. $y-5=-\dfrac{3}{2}(x+2)$

    D. $y+5=-\dfrac{2}{3}(x-2)$
    E. $y+5=-\dfrac{3}{2}(x-2)$

Answer each question below.

20.
(73) *PRSU* and *PQWV* are squares. Find y.

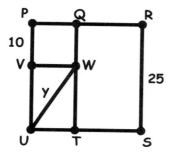

21.
(92) *IJKL* is a square with an area of 36. Find r.

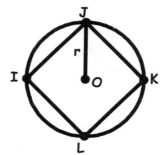

22.
(102) Find r in terms of x, y, m, and n.

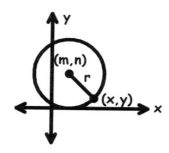

    A. $r=\sqrt{(x-m)^2}+\sqrt{(y-n)^2}$
    B. $r=\sqrt{(x-m)^2+(y-n)^2}$
    C. $r=\sqrt{(x-y)^2+(m-n)^2}$

    D. $r=\sqrt{(x^2-m^2)+(y^2-n^2)}$
    E. $r=\sqrt{(x+m)^2+(y+n)^2}$

153

Do the coordinate proof below.

23. Given: Quadrilateral *PQRS*
(105) Prove: $PS = QR$ and $PQ = SR$

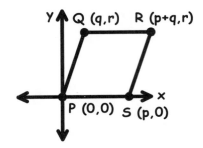

Do the proof below.

24. Given: $\overline{HJ} \parallel \overline{FG}$
Prove: $\overline{JE} \cong \overline{HE}$

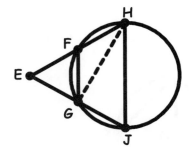

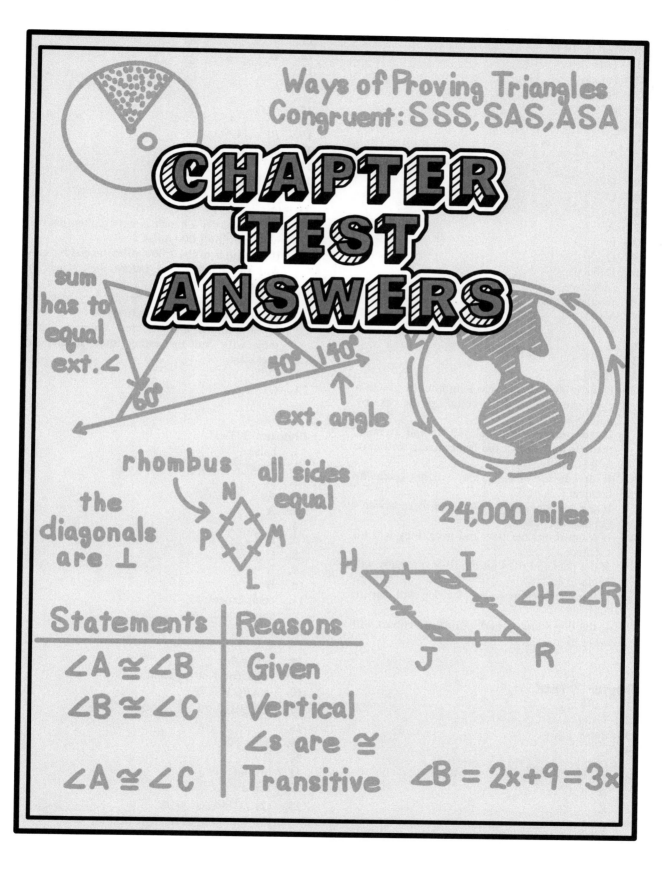

Ways of Proving Triangles
Congruent: SSS, SAS, ASA

CHAPTER TEST ANSWERS

sum has to equal ext. ∠

60°

40° 140°
↑
ext. angle

24,000 miles

rhombus
the diagonals are ⊥

all sides equal

N
P   M
L

H   I
J   R
∠H = ∠R

Statements	Reasons
∠A ≅ ∠B	Given
∠B ≅ ∠C	Vertical ∠s are ≅
∠A ≅ ∠C	Transitive

∠B = 2x + 9 = 3x

Chapter 1 Test
1. True
2. False
3. False
4. B
5. E
6. D
7. A
8. C
9. B
10. C
11. A
12. A
13. E
14. D
15. Deductive
16. Inductive
17. Invalid
18. Valid
19. C
20. E
21. A
22. B
23. If the bride stares for too long into the groom's eyes, she will delay the cutting of the cake by half an hour.
   If the cake-cutting is delayed by half an hour, then Brenda, one of the bridesmaids, will have to leave early.
   If Brenda leaves early, she will not catch the bouquet.
   If she does not catch the bouquet, Brenda won't get married next.
24. If Mom drops her pots and pans, they will hit the floor.
   If the pots and pans hit the floor, the baby will begin to cry.
   If the baby begins to cry, the dog will start to bark.
   If the dog starts to bark, all the neighbors will wake up.

Chapter 2 Test
1. False
2. True
3. False
4. C
5. D
6. C
7. B
8. E
9. A
10. B
11. D
12. A
13. A
14. B
15. $LM = 7\frac{3}{4}$
16. $PV = 14.6$
17. $m\angle MNP = 134$
18. A
19. Valid
20. Invalid
21. C
22. If the explorer's hunch is wrong, then his map will be off by 1,000 miles.
   If his map is off by 1,000 miles, he and his crew will run out of food before they reach the islands.
   If they run out of food before they reach the islands, they will all begin to starve.
   If the explorer and his crew begin to starve, they will end up eating shoe leather for breakfast.
23. D
24. C

Chapter 3 Test
1. False
2. True
3. B
4. A
5. A
6. E
7. D
8. C
9. E
10. B
11. complement: 53
    supplement: 143
12. A
13. C
14. $GH = 46$
15. Adjacent; Not Adjacent
16. $m\angle PQM = 72$
17. $m\angle QNS = 72$
18. 72
19. 60
20. B
21. Invalid
22. Valid
23. (2) $\overline{IJ}$ bisects $\angle LJK$.
    (3) Definition of an angle bisector

(4) $m\angle 1 = \frac{1}{2}m\angle LJK$

(5) Given

(6) Multiplication Property

(7) $m\angle 1 = m\angle 2$

4.	$\overline{QR} \parallel \overline{ST}$	4. If two lines form congruent alternate interior angles with a transversal, then the lines are parallel.

24.

Statements	Reasons
1. $\angle 3$ is complementary to $\angle 1$.	1. Given
2. $\angle 4$ is complementary to $\angle 2$.	2. Given
3. $m\angle 3 = m\angle 4$	3. Pairs of vertical angles are equal.
4. $m\angle 1 = m\angle 2$	4. If two angles are complementary to equal angles, then they are equal.

24.

Statements	Reasons
1. $\overline{BC} \parallel \overline{AD}$, $\overline{AB} \parallel \overline{CD}$	1. Given
2. $m\angle 3 = m\angle 2$, $m\angle 4 = m\angle 1$	2. If two parallel lines are cut by a transversal, then alternate interior angles are equal.
3. $m\angle 3 + m\angle 4 = m\angle 2 + m\angle 1$	3. Addition Property
4. $m\angle BCD = m\angle 3 + m\angle 4$ and $m\angle DAB = m\angle 1 + m\angle 2$	4. Betweenness of Rays
5. $m\angle BCD = m\angle DAB$	5. Substitution Property

Chapter 4 Test

1. True
2. True
3. D
4. A
5. C
6. C
7. E
8. D
9. A
10. C
11. D
12. B
13. B
14. B
15. A
16. $m\angle PTU = 132$
17. $m\angle QTP = 43$
18. $m\angle W = 115$, $m\angle Y = 65$
19. 102, 78
20. 52, 38
21. Valid
22. Invalid
23. Statements

Statements	Reasons
1. $\angle Q \cong \angle S$, $\overline{PQ} \parallel \overline{RS}$	1. Given
2. $\angle Q \cong \angle R$	2. If two parallel lines are cut by a transversal, then their alternate interior angles are congruent.
3. $\angle R \cong \angle S$	3. Transitive Property

Chapter 5 Test

1. False
2. False
3. A
4. C
5. A
6. E
7. B
8. C
9. A
10. D
11. A
12. C
13. $\overline{BC}$, $\overline{CD}$, $\angle ECB$
14. D
15. $m\angle A = 70$, $m\angle B = 50$, $m\angle C = 60$
16. B
17. $x = 52$, $y = 23$
18. $y = 52$
19. $x = 77$
20. $x = 128$, $y = 45$
21. A
22. D
23. Statements

Statements	Reasons
1. $\overline{JK} \perp \overline{KL}$, $\overline{JM} \perp \overline{ML}$, $\angle KJL \cong \angle MJL$	1. Given
2. $\angle K$ and $\angle M$ are right angles.	2. Perpendicular lines intersect to form right angles.

3. $\angle K \cong \angle M$ | 3. All right angles are congruent.
4. $\overline{JL} \cong \overline{JL}$ | 4. Reflexive Property
5. $\triangle JKL \cong \triangle JML$ | 5. Angle-Angle-Side

24.

Statements	Reasons
1. $\overline{AF} \perp \overline{BD}$, $\overline{CE} \perp \overline{BD}$	1. Given
2. $\angle AFB$ and $\angle CED$ are right angles.	2. Perpendicular lines intersect to form right angles.
3. $\triangle ABF$ and $\triangle CDE$ are right triangles.	3. Definition of a right triangle
4. $BE = BF + FE$ and $FD = DE + FE$	4. Betweenness of Points
5. $BE = FD$	5. Given
6. $BF + FE = DE + FE$	6. Substitution Property
7. $BF = DE$	7. Subtraction Property
8. $AB = CD$	8. Given
9. $\triangle ABF \cong \triangle CDE$	9. Hypotenuse-Leg

Chapter 6 Test

1. True
2. False
3. D
4. C
5. D
6. A
7. A
8. E
9. B
10. B
11. E
12. C
13. 88, 46, 46
14. D
15. A
16. $x = 25$
17. $x = 14$, $y = 55$
18. $x = 25$, $y = 10$
19. 22.5
20. 133, 47
21. B
22. E

23.

Statements	Reasons
1. $\overline{KM} \parallel \overline{JH}$, $\overline{KM} \cong \overline{JH}$, $\overline{JK} \cong \overline{KL}$	1. Given
2. $\angle HJK \cong \angle MKL$	2. If parallel lines are cut by a transversal,

	then corresponding angles are congruent.
3. $\triangle HJK \cong \triangle MKL$	3. Side-Angle-Side
4. $\angle JKH \cong \angle KLM$	4. C.P.C.T.C.
5. $\overline{HK} \parallel \overline{ML}$	5. If two lines form congruent corresponding angles with a transversal, then the lines are parallel.

24.

Statements	Reasons
1. $\triangle ABC$; $\overline{CA} \cong \overline{CB}$; $\overline{AD}$ and $\overline{BE}$ are altitudes of $\triangle ABC$.	1. Given
2. $\angle ADB$ and $\angle BEA$ are right angles.	2. Definition of an altitude
3. $\angle ADB \cong \angle BEA$	3. All right angles are congruent.
4. $\angle ABC \cong \angle BAC$	4. Base Angles Theorem
5. $\overline{AB} \cong \overline{AB}$	5. Reflexive Property
6. $\triangle ADB \cong \triangle BEA$	6. Angle-Angle-Side
7. $\overline{AD} \cong \overline{BE}$	7. C.P.C.T.C.

Chapter 7 Test

1. False
2. True
3. D
4. A
5. C
6. E
7. **a.** No; **b.** Yes
8. **a.** Greater than 5 and less than 9; **b.** Greater than 9 and less than 33
9. C
10. C
11. 32, 32, 116
12. 10, 80, 90
13. Converse: False
Inverse: False
Contrapositive: True
14. Converse: False
Inverse: False
Contrapositive: True
15. D
16. B
17. B
18. $\angle I$
19. $m + n = 140$

20. $x = 7.5$, $y = 75$
21. $x = 42$
22. $a = 85$
23. Statements

Statements		Reasons
1.	$\overline{PQ} \cong \overline{PR}$	1. Given
2.	$\angle 3 \cong \angle 4$	2. Base Angles Theorem
3.	$\overline{QR} \parallel \overline{ST}$	3. Given
4.	$\angle 1 \cong \angle 3$ and $\angle 2 \cong \angle 4$	4. If two parallel lines are cut by a transversal, then their corresponding angles are congruent.
5.	$\angle 1 \cong \angle 4$	5. Transitive Property
6.	$\angle 1 \cong \angle 2$	6. Transitive Property
7.	$\overline{SP} \cong \overline{TP}$	7. Converse of the Base Angles Theorem
8.	$\triangle SPT$ is isosceles.	8. Definition of an isosceles triangle

24. Statements

Statements		Reasons
1.	$IJ = KJ$	1. Given
2.	Either $IL = LM$ or $IL \neq LM$. Assume $IL = LM$.	2. A statement is either true or false.
3.	$m\angle 1 = m\angle 2$	3. Base Angles Theorem
4.	$m\angle 1 > m\angle K$	4. Exterior Angle Inequality Theorem
5.	$m\angle 2 > m\angle K$	5. Substitution Property of Inequality
6.	$m\angle JIK > m\angle 2$	6. Whole Greater Than Its Part Property
7.	$m\angle JIK > m\angle K$	7. Transitive Property of Inequality
8.	$IJ < KJ$	8. If Unequal Angles, Then Unequal Sides
9.	$IL \neq LM$	9. Statement 8 contradicts the given statement that $IJ = KJ$. The assumption made in statement 2 must be false. By elimination, statement 9 must be true.

Chapter 8 Test
1. False
2. True

3. C
4. E
5. E
6. C
7. B
8. A
9. D
10. A
11. B
12. Converse: False
Inverse: False
Contrapositive: True
13. Converse: False
Inverse: False
Contrapositive: True
14. E
15. B
16. A
17. $x = 3$, $y = 120$, $z = 120$
18. $x = 9$
19. $y = 75$
20. $m\angle R = 110$, $m\angle S = 70$
21. $\angle G$
22. $m\angle K = 35$, $m\angle L = 105$
23. Statements

Statements		Reasons
1.	Rectangle $EJHG$	1. Given
2.	$\overline{EJ} \cong \overline{GH}$	2. Both pairs of opposite sides of a rectangle are congruent.
3.	$\angle J \cong \angle G$	3. Both pairs of opposite angles of a rectangle/parallelogram are congruent.
4.	$\overline{JI} \cong \overline{FG}$	4. Given
5.	$\triangle JEI \cong \triangle GHF$	5. Side-Angle-Side
6.	$\overline{EI} \cong \overline{HF}$	6. C.P.C.T.C.

24. Statements

Statements		Reasons
1.	$\triangle NOP \cong \triangle QRP$	1. Given
2.	$\overline{NO} \cong \overline{QR}$	2. C.P.C.T.C.
3.	N is the midpoint of $\overline{MO}$.	3. Given
4.	$\overline{MN} \cong \overline{NO}$	4. Definition of a midpoint
5.	$\overline{MN} \cong \overline{QR}$	5. Transitive Property
6.	$\angle O \cong \angle PRQ$	6. C.P.C.T.C.
7.	$\overline{MN} \parallel \overline{QR}$	7. If two lines form congruent alternate interior angles with a transversal, then the lines are parallel.

8. *MNQR* is a parallel-ogram.

8. If one pair of opposite sides is both parallel and congruent, then a quadrilateral is a parallelogram.

Chapter 9 Test

1. True
2. True
3. A
4. D
5. B
6. E
7. B
8. E
9. E
10. C
11. A
12. D
13. 360
14. A
15. C
16. Converse: False
   Inverse: False
   Contrapositive: True
17. perimeter $= 34$
18. perimeter $= 126$
19. $x + y = 170$
20. $x = 125$
21. $a + b + c + d = 230$
22. $x = 5$, $y = 6$

23.

Statements	Reasons
1. *GCDE* is a rectangle.	1. Given
2. $\overline{CE} \cong \overline{GD}$	2. The diagonals of a rectangle are congruent.
3. *GCEF* is a parallelogram.	3. Given
4. $\overline{CE} \cong \overline{GF}$	4. If a quadrilateral is a parallelogram, then both pairs of opposite sides are congruent.
5. $\overline{GD} \cong \overline{GF}$	5. Transitive Property
6. $\triangle GDF$ is isosceles.	6. Definition of an isosceles triangle

24.

Statements	Reasons
1. *PQRS* is a parallelo-gram.	1. Given

2. $\overline{PQ} \cong \overline{RS}$

2. If a quadrilateral is a parallelogram, then both pairs of opposite sides are congruent.

3. $\angle P \cong \angle R$

3. If a quadrilateral is a parallelogram, then both pairs of opposite angles are congruent.

4. $\overline{TQ} \perp \overline{QR}$, $\overline{US} \perp \overline{PS}$

4. Given

5. $\angle TQR$ and $\angle PSU$ are right angles.

5. Perpendicular lines intersect to form right angles.

6. $\overline{QR} \parallel \overline{PS}$

6. Definition of a parallelogram

7. $\angle TQR \cong \angle QTP$ and $\angle PSU \cong \angle SUR$

7. If two parallel lines are cut by a transversal, then their alternate interior angles are congruent.

8. $\angle QTP$ and $\angle SUR$ are right angles.

8. Congruent angles have equal measures.

9. $\angle QTP \cong \angle SUR$

9. All right angles are congruent.

10. $\triangle QTP \cong \triangle SUR$

10. Angle-Angle-Side

Chapter 10 Test

1. True
2. False
3. D
4. C
5. E
6. **a.** Yes; **b.** Yes; **c.** No
7. $r = 9$
8. 8
9. $\dfrac{IL}{JL} = \dfrac{7}{3}$; $\dfrac{IM}{KM} = \dfrac{7}{3}$; Sides are divided propor-tionally.
10. 30 feet
11. 32 cm
12. D
13. A
14. Not similar
15. D
16. A
17. C
18. perimeter $= 6$
19. $y = 38$
20. $y = 30$
21. $MO = 12$, $PR = 3$

22. $PN = 3$, $IM = 5$

23.

Statements	Reasons
1. $\overline{MN} \cong \overline{NO}$	1. Given
2. $\angle M \cong \angle O$	2. Base Angles Theorem
3. $\overline{GH} \perp \overline{MO}$, $\overline{PQ} \perp \overline{MO}$	3. Given
4. $\angle GHO$ and $\angle PQM$ are right angles.	4. Perpendicular lines intersect to form right angles.
5. $\angle GHO \cong \angle PQM$	5. All right angles are congruent.
6. $\triangle GHO \sim \triangle PQM$	6. Angle-Angle Similarity

24.

Statements	Reasons
1. $\triangle ORC \sim \triangle FEH$	1. Given
2. $m\angle ORC = m\angle FEH$	2. Converse of the definition of similar triangles
3. $\frac{1}{2}m\angle ORC = \frac{1}{2}m\angle FEH$	3. Multiplication Property
4. $\overline{RT}$ bisects $\angle ORC$, and $\overline{EG}$ bisects $\angle FEH$.	4. Given
5. $\frac{1}{2}m\angle ORC = m\angle TRC$ and $\frac{1}{2}m\angle FEH = m\angle GEH$	5. Definition of an angle bisector
6. $m\angle TRC = m\angle GEH$	6. Substitution Property
7. $m\angle C = m\angle H$	7. Converse of the definition of similar triangles
8. $\triangle RTC \sim \triangle EGH$	8. Angle-Angle Similarity

Chapter 11 Test

1. True
2. False
3. A
4. E
5. A
6. $5\sqrt{3}$, 8.65
7. $8\sqrt{2}$, 11.28
8. Yes
9. No
10. $x = 4$

11. $x = 12$
12. $x = 10$
13. $y = 17.30$
14. 0.47
15. 0.91
16. $x = 11.55$
17. $y = 6.43$
18. 13 feet
19. $x = 18$
20. $y = 10\sqrt{2}$
21. 19.59 meters
22. 890.99 miles

23.

Statements	Reasons
1. $\triangle FCE \sim \triangle HID$	1. Given
2. $\angle CEF \cong \angle IDH$	2. Converse of the definition of similar triangles
3. $\overline{GD}$ bisects $\angle IDF$.	3. Given
4. $\angle IDH \cong \angle HDC$	4. Definition of an angle bisector
5. $\angle CEF \cong \angle HDC$	5. Transitive Property
6. $\angle FCE \cong \angle HCD$	6. Pairs of vertical angles are congruent.
7. $\triangle FCE \sim \triangle HCD$	7. Angle-Angle Similarity

24.

Statements	Reasons
1. $PCDE$ is a parallelogram.	1. Given
2. $\overline{PC} \cong \overline{ED}$ and $\overline{PE} \cong \overline{CD}$	2. Opposite sides of a parallelogram are congruent.
3. $\overline{PC} \parallel \overline{ED}$ and $\overline{PE} \parallel \overline{CD}$	3. Definition of a parallelogram
4. $\angle FPC \cong \angle GDE$ and $\angle FPE \cong \angle GDC$	4. If two parallel lines are cut by a transversal, then their alternate interior angles are congruent.
5. $\overline{PF} \cong \overline{DG}$	5. Given
6. $\triangle PFC \cong \triangle DGE$ and $\triangle PFE \cong \triangle DGC$	6. Side-Angle-Side
7. $\overline{FE} \cong \overline{GC}$ and $\overline{GE} \cong \overline{FC}$	7. C.P.C.T.C.
8. $FCGE$ is a parallelogram.	8. If both pairs of opposite sides are congruent, then a quadrilateral is a parallelogram.

Chapter 12 Test
1. True
2. False
3. C
4. D
5. A
6. E
7. D
8. A
9. $m\angle EOF = 124$
10. $m\widehat{DGF} = 193$
11. $\ell\widehat{PQ} = 9\pi$
12. $\ell\widehat{TSU} = 14\pi$
13. $m\angle IMJ = 62.5$
14. $m\angle DPR = 46$
15. $IM = 6$
16. $ST = 5$
17. $x = 6$
18. $y = 116$
19. $x = 12\sqrt{3}$
20. $d = 65$
21. A
22. E
23. Statements · Reasons

Statements	Reasons
1. $\overline{IK}$ and $\overline{IM}$ are secant segments.	1. Given
2. $IK \times IJ = IM \times IL$	2. If two secant segments are drawn to a circle from the same exterior point, then the product of the lengths of one secant segment and its external segment is equal to the product of the lengths of the other secant segment and its external segment.
3. $IK = IM$	3. Given
4. $IM \times IJ = IM \times IL$	4. Substitution Property
5. $IJ = IL$	5. Division Property

24. Statements · Reasons

Statements	Reasons
1. Draw radii $\overline{OR}$ and $\overline{OS}$ of $\odot O$.	1. Two points determine a unique straight line.
2. $\overline{OR} \cong \overline{OS}$	2. All radii of the same circle are congruent.
3. $\widehat{RP} \cong \widehat{PS}$	3. Given

Statements	Reasons
4. $m\widehat{RP} = m\angle ROP$ and $m\widehat{PS} = m\angle POS$	4. The degree measure of a minor arc is the measure of its central angle.
5. $\angle ROP \cong \angle POS$	5. Substitution Property
6. $\overline{OT} \cong \overline{OT}$	6. Reflexive Property
7. $\triangle OTR \cong \triangle OTS$	7. Side-Angle-Side
8. $\overline{ST} \cong \overline{RT}$	8. C.P.C.T.C.

Chapter 13 Test
1. False
2. True
3. D
4. D
5. B
6. area = 105 in.^{2}
7. area = 1,200 cm^2
8. area = 24
9. area = 36
10. area = 18
11. area = 112
12. area = 88
13. area = 12
14. area = 78
15. area = 153 cm^2
16. area = 60 in.^{2}
17. area = 252 m^2
18. area = 18 ft.^{2}
19. area = 252π
20. area = 24π
21. area = 1,080
22. $x = 6$
23. Statements · Reasons

Statements	Reasons
1. $\overline{LK} \cong \overline{IJ}$	1. Given
2. $m\widehat{LK} = m\widehat{IJ}$	2. If two chords of the same circle are congruent, then their minor arcs are congruent.
3. $m\widehat{LK} + m\widehat{JK} = m\widehat{IJ} + m\widehat{JK}$	3. Addition Property
4. $m\widehat{LK} + m\widehat{JK} = m\widehat{LJ}$ and $m\widehat{IJ} + m\widehat{JK} = m\widehat{IK}$	4. Arc Addition Postulate
5. $m\widehat{LJ} = m\widehat{IK}$	5. Substitution Property
6. $\overline{LJ} \cong \overline{IK}$	6. If two minor arcs of the same circle are congruent, then their intersecting chords are congruent.

24.

Statements	Reasons
1. $\overline{PR}$ is tangent to $\odot O$ at P and $\overline{QR}$ is tangent to $\odot O$ at Q.	1. Given
2. $\overline{PR} \cong \overline{QR}$	2. If two tangent segments are drawn to a circle from the same exterior point, then they are congruent.
3. $\angle RPO$ and $\angle RQO$ are right angles.	3. If a radius is drawn to the point of tangency of a tangent line, then the radius is perpendicular to the tangent line.
4. $\triangle RPO$ and $\triangle RQO$ are right triangles.	4. Definition of a right triangle
5. $\overline{RO} \cong \overline{RO}$	5. Reflexive Property
6. $\triangle RPO \cong \triangle RQO$	6. Hypotenuse-Leg
7. $\angle PRO \cong \angle QRO$	7. C.P.C.T.C.
8. $\overline{RS}$ bisects $\angle PRQ$.	8. Definition of an angle bisector

Chapter 14 Test
1. False
2. True
3. E
4. B
5. C
6. area $= 48\pi$
7. A
8. D
9. Surface Area $= 416$ in.^{2}; Vol. $= 480$ in.^{3}
10. Surface Area $= 964$ cm^2; Vol. $= 1{,}872$ cm^3
11. D
12. A
13. total area $= 228$
14. total area $= 485$
15. surface area $= 324\pi$
16. total area $= 320$
17. volume $= 16{,}261$
18. volume $= 2{,}187\pi$
19. volume $= 105$
20. $n = 100$
21. $c = 45$
22. $64 : 1$

23.

Statements	Reasons
1. $\overline{KL} \parallel \overline{IJ}$	1. Given
2. Draw $\overline{LI}$.	2. Two points determine a unique straight line.
3. $m\angle KLI = m\angle JIL$	3. If two parallel lines are cut by a transversal, then their alternate interior angles are equal.
4. $m\angle KLI = \frac{1}{2}m\widehat{IK}$ and $m\angle JIL = \frac{1}{2}m\widehat{JL}$	4. An inscribed angle is equal in measure to one-half the measure of its intercepted arc.
5. $\frac{1}{2}m\widehat{IK} = \frac{1}{2}m\widehat{JL}$	5. Substitution Property
6. $m\widehat{IK} = m\widehat{JL}$	6. Multiplication Property
7. $\widehat{IK} \cong \widehat{JL}$	7. Arcs with equal measures are congruent.

24.

Statements	Reasons
1. $\overline{OP}$ is an apothem of regular polygon $JKLMN$.	1. Given
2. $\overline{OP} \perp \overline{KL}$	2. Definition of an apothem of a regular polygon
3. $\angle OPK$ and $\angle OPL$ are right angles.	3. Perpendicular lines intersect to form right angles
4. $\triangle OPK$ and $\triangle OPL$ are right triangles.	4. Definition of a right triangle
5. Draw radii $\overline{OK}$ and $\overline{OL}$.	5. Two points determine a unique straight line.
6. $\overline{OK} \cong \overline{OL}$	6. Definition of the radius of a regular polygon
7. $\overline{OP} \cong \overline{OP}$	7. Reflexive Property
8. $\triangle KPO \cong \triangle LPO$	8. Hypotenuse-Leg
9. $\overline{KP} \cong \overline{LP}$	9. C.P.C.T.C.
10. $\overline{OP}$ bisects $\overline{KL}$.	10. Definition of a segment bisector

Chapter 15 Test
1. False
2. True
3. A
4. D
5. D
6. $H(-2,3)$ and $F(2,-2)$

7. $P(-a,a)$ and $Q(0,a)$

8. C

9. area = 16

10. E

11. $\left(0,-\dfrac{5}{2}\right)$

12. $WS = 3$

13. C

14. E

15. Slope of line E: $-\dfrac{7}{6}$; Slope of line F: 1

16. total area = 816 cm^2

17. volume = 720

18. B

19. E

20. $y = 5\sqrt{13}$

21. $r = 3\sqrt{2}$

22. B

23. Quadrilateral $PQRS$ (Given). The lengths of the horizontal legs are $PS = p$ and $QR = p + q - q = p$ (The length of a horizontal line segment is the absolute value of the difference in the x values of the end points), so $PS = QR$ by the Transitive Property. Also, by the Distance Formula, $PQ = \sqrt{(q-0)^2 + (r-0)^2} = \sqrt{q^2 + r^2}$ and $RS = \sqrt{(p+q-p)^2 + (r-0)^2} = \sqrt{q^2 + r^2}$. So by the Transitive Property $PQ = SR$.

6.	$m\widehat{JG} = m\widehat{HF}$	6. Multiplication Property
7.	$m\widehat{FG} = m\widehat{FG}$	7. Reflexive Property
8.	$m\widehat{JG} + m\widehat{FG} = m\widehat{HF} + m\widehat{FG}$	8. Addition Property
9.	$m\widehat{JGF} = m\widehat{JG} + m\widehat{FG}$ and $m\widehat{HFG} = m\widehat{HF} + m\widehat{FG}$	9. Arc Addition Postulate
10.	$m\widehat{JGF} = m\widehat{HFG}$	10. Substitution Property
11.	$\angle EHJ \cong \angle EJH$	11. Inscribed angles that intercept congruent arcs are congruent.
12.	$\overline{JE} \cong \overline{HE}$	12. Converse of the Base Angles Theorem

24.

	Statements	Reasons
1.	$\overline{HJ} \parallel \overline{FG}$	1. Given
2.	Draw chord HG.	2. Two points determine a unique straight line.
3.	$m\angle JHG = m\angle HGF$	3. If two parallel lines are cut by a transversal, then their alternate interior angles are equal.
4.	$m\angle JHG = \dfrac{1}{2}m\widehat{JG}$ and $m\angle HGF = \dfrac{1}{2}m\widehat{HF}$	4. An inscribed angle is equal in measure to one-half the measure of its intercepted arc.
5.	$\dfrac{1}{2}m\widehat{JG} = \dfrac{1}{2}m\widehat{HF}$	5. Substitution Property